Dave Ramsey's

Financial Peace® UNIVERSITY

MISSION STATEMENT:

To empower and give HOPE to everyone from the financially secure to the financially distressed.

1749 Mallory Lane, Suite 100 • Brentwood, TN 37027.

Published by THE LAMPO GROUP, INC. For more information, please contact DAVE RAMSEY's office at 888.22.PEACE.

About the Founder of FPU

Dave Ramsey is a personal money management expert, an extremely popular national radio personality, and the best-selling author of *The Total Money Makeover.* In his latest book, a follow-up of his enormously successful *New York Times* best-sellers *Financial Peace* and *More Than Enough,* Ramsey exemplifies his life's work of teaching others how to be financially responsible so they can acquire enough wealth to take care of loved ones, live prosperously into old age, and give generously to others.

Ramsey knows first-hand what financial peace means in his own life—living a true rags-to-riches-to-rags-to-riches story. By age 26 he had established a four-million-dollar real estate portfolio, only to lose it by age 30. He has since rebuilt his financial life and now devotes himself full-time to helping ordinary people understand the forces behind their financial distress and how to set things right—financially, emotionally, and spiritually.

Ramsey offers life-changing financial advice as host of a nationally syndicated radio program, "The Dave Ramsey Show," which is heard by more than three million listeners each week on more than 300 radio stations throughout the United States.

Ramsey is the creator of *Financial Peace University* (FPU), a 13-week program that helps people dump their debt, get control of their money, and learn new behaviors around money that are founded on commitment and accountability. More than half a million families have attended FPU classes at their workplace, church, military base, local nonprofit organization, community group, or Spanish-speaking organization. The average family pays off $5,300 in debt and saves $2,700 in the first 91 days after beginning FPU and is completely out of debt, except for the mortgage, in 18 to 24 months.

Ramsey created a group of products in an effort to teach children about money before they have a chance to make mistakes. *Financial Peace for the Next Generation* is an all-inclusive school curriculum that is currently in more than 1,300 schools across the country. *Financial Peace Jr.* is an instructional kit designed to help parents teach their young children about working, saving, and giving their own money. Through Ramsey's entertaining children's book series, *The Super Red Racer, Careless at the Carnival, The Big Birthday Surprise, My Fantastic Fieldtrip, A Special Thank You,* and *Battle of the Chores,* children learn about working, saving, giving, budgeting, integrity, and debt.

Ramsey earned his B.S. degree in Finance and Real Estate from the University of Tennessee. A frequent speaker around the country at large-scale live events, Ramsey is a passionate and inspiring presenter who is at ease on both sides of the microphone. More than 400,000 people have attended Ramsey's live events.

TABLE OF CONTENTS

Getting Started

Weekly Lessons

Additional Resources

Financial Forms

Dave Ramsey's
Financial Peace UNIVERSITY

Getting Started

How Well Are We Handling Money Today?

- Only 32% of Americans would be able to cover a $5,000 emergency with cash without going into debt for it.

  - Gallup/Bankrate.com survey

- A *Parenting Magazine* poll indicates that 49% could not cover even one month's expenses if they were to miss a paycheck.

- Bankruptcies in 2005 totaled 2,078,415. Of those, 79% were total Chapter 7 bankruptcies.

  - U.S. Bankruptcy Courts, http://www.uscourts.gov/bnkrpctystats/statistics.htm#june

- Total consumer debt hit $2.7 trillion in April 2006, the highest in history.

  - Federal Reserve Statistical Release, June 7, 2006

- 60% of working Americans experience moderate to high levels of financial stress. One-fifth of those believe their financial stress has gotten worse in the last 18-24 months.

  - 2004 National Omnibus Survey, reported in Ameriprise.com

- 53% of Americans have less than $25,000 in retirement savings. 43% of those people are over 55! 30% believe that they only need $250,000 or less in total retirement savings.

  - Retirement Confidence Survey, 2006

- When asked how they make their retirement planning decisions, 44% of working Americans say they "guess."

  - Retirement Confidence Survey, 2006

- Savings rate for 2006 was -1%, the lowest since the Great Depression.

  - Bureau of Economic Analysis: U.S. Department of Commerce, January, 2006

Imagine... Having absolutely no debt—no car payments, no credit card payments, not even a house payment. How would it feel to actually get to keep your money instead of mailing it out to a dozen creditors month after month?

Imagine... Retiring with a nest egg of almost six million dollars. Don't laugh—a 30-year-old couple with an average household income of $40,000 can get there by investing only $500 a month from age 30 to 70.

Imagine... Breaking the family curse of financial poverty, stress, and insecurity. What could your children and your children's children accomplish if you set the family free from the bondage of debt and money mismanagement?

• • •

This is the FUTURE, and it could be YOURS if...

You are sick and tired of being sick and tired.

You want to be ready for emergencies.

You are ready to beat debt and build wealth.

You are willing to do what it takes today in order to win tomorrow.

• • •

It's time to change your behavior, take control of your money, and finally take your place on the road to

Financial Peace!

Things to keep in mind . . .

BALANCE

Balance is crucial to success. Don't only focus on money; be sure to keep your physical, mental, and spiritual health as high priorities in your life. Regular exercise, prayer, quiet meditation, reading, and FUN are all great stress relievers! Plus, make sure you have a solid network of friends to support you as you go about the often-difficult day-to-day details of your new plan.

FAMILY

If you're married, it is absolutely critical that you and your spouse be on the same page with your money. THIS CANNOT BE OVERSTATED. Couples must be in agreement on spending, saving, debt reduction, and long-term planning or your plan will fail. Financial stress is consistently one of the leading causes of marital problems in North America. You've got to protect your relationship. Do NOT let money fights destroy your marriage!

Spend quality time alone with your spouse. If you do not already have a "date night," start one immediately! Also, allow your children to participate in the family's financial turnaround. Lead by example, stressing the importance of avoiding debt for the rest of their lives.

CREDITORS AND FINANCIAL PRIORITIES

If you are standing in the midst of a financial nightmare, and/or if you are currently dealing with collections pressure, just hold on tight! The FPU course will teach you how to get through this.

In the meantime, do NOT allow anyone else to set your family's financial priorities. It is YOUR responsibility to take care of necessities first. We call this the Four Walls—food, clothing, shelter, and transportation. The well-being of your family comes first, no matter who or what else is clamoring for your money.

IT STARTS NOW!

Do not write any more bad checks. Do not buy anything that you can't pay for with cash. Do not go one more penny into debt. ***Your new way of life starts right now!***

Here's a checklist of tools and concepts that will help you succeed:

- ***Baby Steps***
  In the first lesson of FPU, you'll learn Dave's seven tried-and-true steps for getting out of debt and into long-term wealth.

- ***Online Resources***
  From budgeting software to exclusive video content, your FPU membership includes a ton of online tools and resources.

- ***Reading Assignments***
  Each FPU lesson is tied to specific sections of Dave's bestseller, *Financial Peace Revisited.* Use this text to reinforce what you're learning in class each week.

- ***Envelope System***
  Dave will show you how to organize your regular expenses like food, gas, and clothing with the cash-based envelope system.

- ***Quickie Budget***
  After the first lesson, you'll be asked to start a household budget—possibly for the first time. The Basic Quickie Budget (in the forms section of this workbook) makes it easy to get started.

- ***Monthly Budgets***
  After the third lesson, you'll be responsible for maintaining a monthly household budget. Your class coordinator and classmates will hold you accountable for this, so you better do it!

- ***Buddy System***
  Don't try to go it alone! Find a buddy to connect with and confide in.

- ***Accountability***
  Share openly with your classmates and give them permission to hold you accountable to your plan.

- ***Financial Snapshot***
  These regular snapshots will help you track your progress over the 13 weeks of FPU. You can use the included paper form or take your snapshots online.

- ***Giving***
  Something wonderful happens to the human spirit when you become a generous giver. Cultivate the habit by giving to your church or other worthy causes.

Understanding This Book

This workbook will guide you through each part of *Financial Peace University*. Within these pages, you'll find notes and critical information for each of the 13 class sessions, which you will use to follow along with Dave's teaching by video. You'll also find more than a dozen different budget forms, links to online-only resources, a glossary of related financial terms, class discussion questions, goal-setting tips and challenges, and more!

As you work through this book, you'll see four different graphical icons to help keep you focused throughout the course. Be sure to watch for the following:

The **lighthouse** icon indicates a point of wisdom and insight. Here, you'll find important notes and quotations that clarify, support, and enhance what you're learning in class.

The **book** icon represents old proverbs and scriptural wisdom. This gives you a new perspective as you learn to see the impact money has on your relationships, business, priorities, and personal growth.

The **computer** icon reveals special online-only resources specifically designed to correspond with your FPU class. At **daveramsey.com/fpumember**, you'll find resources tailored to each lesson, bringing you additional training opportunities, budgeting tools, supplemental audio and video pieces, and other lesson-specific downloads.

The **gazelle** icon represents activity and "Gazelle Intensity," which Dave will explain in the first lesson. Whenever you see this gazelle, you'll be called to do something, such as set a personal goal or review your budget.

Enhance your FPU experience with these great online-only features:

- ***Budget Software***
  Our Gazelle Budget software leads you step by step, helping you build a budget, track expenses, eliminate debt, and plan for your future!

- ***Up-To-Date Stats***
  Get the most recent stats online. We'll update each lesson's statistical information whenever there's a new study, report, or additional information available.

- ***Exclusive Videos***
  Watch special messages from Dave, inspiring mini-documentaries, and exclusive clips from Dave's live events as you work through each week of FPU!

- ***Community Forums***
  Take your small group discussions to the world! Enjoy general conversations or discuss the details of each lesson with others who are working through FPU.

- ***Download Forms***
  Download and print all of the FPU budget forms on demand! You can even use these forms to help other people take control of their money.

- ***Extra Tools***
  You have access to an online financial glossary, calculators, inspiring testimonies, budgeting tips, and tons of other lesson-specific content and resources!

YOUR FPU CLASS CODE:

Get your class code from your FPU Class Coordinator. You will need this class code to access all of the additional online resources of the FPU Member Resource Center.

Start using these FREE resources today at
daveramsey.com/fpumember

Dave Ramsey's
Financial Peace® UNIVERSITY

Super Saving™

Common Sense for Your Dollars and Cents

The Seven Baby Steps

You can get anywhere if you simply go one step at a time.

"If you do the things you need to do when you need to do them, then someday you can do the things you want to do when you want to do them."

– Zig Ziglar

There is a process for getting out of the mess that we created without feeling overwhelmed. Getting out of debt will not happen overnight; it takes time. Here are the Baby Steps that will get you started:

Step 1: $1,000 in an emergency fund ($500 if your income is under $20,000 per year)

Step 2: Pay off all debt except the house utilizing the debt snowball (found in the Dumping Debt lesson)

Step 3: Three to six months expenses in savings

Step 4: Invest 15% of your household income into Roth IRAs and pre-tax retirement plans

Step 5: College funding

Step 6: Pay off your home early

Step 7: Build wealth and give!

If you will live like no one else,
later you can live like no one else.

Baby Step 1™

$__________ in the bank.

If your income is under $20,000, make this $______.

- Saving must become a ____________________.
- You must pay yourself ____________________.
- Give, save, then pay ____________________.
- Saving money is about ____________________ and ____________________.
- Building wealth is not evil or wrong. Money is __________.
- Larry Burkett, a famous Christian author, said, "The only difference in saving and hoarding is ____________________."

You should save for three basic reasons:

1. ____________________ __________
2. ____________________
3. ____________________ ____________

"For the love of money is a root of all kinds of evil."

– 1 Timothy 6:10 (NIV)

"In the house of the wise are stores of choice food and oil, but a foolish man devours all he has."

– Proverbs 21:20 (NIV)

NOTES

Emergency Fund

______________ events do occur—expect them!

Remember: Baby Step 1, a beginner emergency fund, is $__________ in the bank (or $500 if your household income is below $20,000 per year).

Baby Step 3™

__ to __ months of expenses in savings.

A great place to keep your emergency fund is in a ___________ ____________ account from a mutual fund company.

Your emergency fund is not an _________________; it is ___________________.

Do not ________________ this fund for purchases.

The emergency fund is your ______________ savings priority. Do it quickly!

"And let them gather all the food of those good years that are coming, and store up grain under the authority of Pharaoh, and let them keep food in the cities. Then that food shall be as a reserve for the land for the seven years of famine which shall be in the land of Egypt, that the land may not perish during the famine."

– Genesis 41:35-36 (NKJV)

In our lives, we all go through "times of famine." Whether it's a layoff, lengthy illness, large financial loss, etc., we need to be prepared and save up while we can. It will allow us to better cope during tough times and, in some cases, to survive.

Purchases

Instead of ___________________ to purchase, pay cash by using a ___________________ fund approach.

For example...

Say you borrow to purchase a $ _____________ dining room set. Most furniture stores will sell their financing contracts to finance companies.

This means you will have borrowed at _______%
with payments of $________ per month for _______ months.
So, you will pay a total of $________, plus insurance, for that set.

But if you save the same $________ per month for only ______ months, you will be able to pay cash.

When you pay cash, you can almost always negotiate a discount, so you will be able to buy it even earlier.

> One definition of maturity is learning to delay pleasure. Children do what feels good; adults devise a plan and follow it.

NOTES

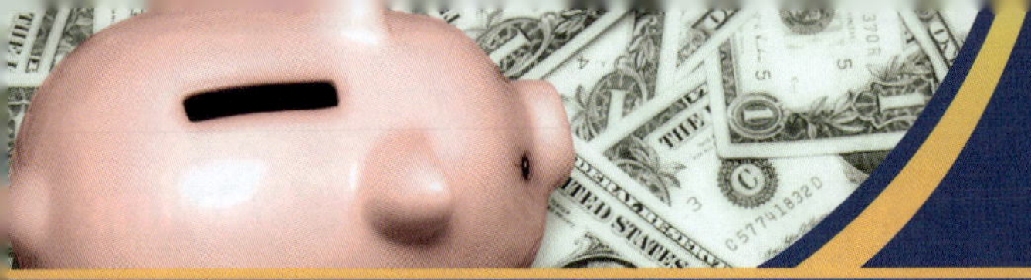

Save for a $4,600 car by putting $_________ per month in the cookie jar for only 10 months!

Since we have pledged to borrow no more, this is the only way to make a purchase.

If your teenager really got this lesson early and ***never*** had a car payment throughout his whole life, do you realize how wealthy he could become just from this ***one decision?***

Go online to learn how to drive FREE CARS for the rest of your life! Check out ***"Drive Free, Retire Rich"*** in this week's online resources.

Wealth Building

Retirement & College Funding, Etc.

__________________ is a key ingredient.

Building wealth is a _______________, not a ____________.

Just $_______ per month, every month, from age 25 to age 65, at _____% will build to over $________________.

"No discipline seems pleasant at the time, but painful. Later on, however, it produces a harvest of righteousness and peace for those who have been trained by it." – Hebrews 12:11 (NIV)

____________________ ______________ (PACs) withdrawals are a good way to build in discipline.

Compound interest is a mathematical ____________.

You must start ______________ !

Daily decisions can make a HUGE impact!

Expense	Cost per day	Cost per month	If invested at 12% from age 16-76
Cigarettes	$3	$90	$11,622,000
Gourmet Coffee	$5	$150	$19,371,943
Lunch (5 days/week)	$8	$160	$20,663,319

Is it worth the cost in the long run?

"A faithful man will abound with blessings, but he who hastens to be rich will not go unpunished."

– Proverbs 28:20 (NKJV)

You will either learn to manage money, or the lack of it will always manage you.

NOTES

"If riches increase, do not set your heart on them."

– Psalm 62:10 (NKJV)

The Story of Ben and Arthur

Both save $2,000 per year at 12%. Ben starts at age 19 and stops at age 26, while Arthur starts at age 27 and stops at age 65.

Age	Ben Invests:		Arthur Invests:	
19	2,000	2,240	0	0
20	2,000	4,749	0	0
21	2,000	7,558	0	0
22	2,000	10,706	0	0
23	2,000	14,230	0	0
24	2,000	18,178	0	0
25	2,000	22,599	0	0
26	2,000	27,551	0	0
27	0	30,857	2,000	2,240
28	0	34,560	2,000	4,749
29	0	38,708	2,000	7,558
30	0	43,352	2,000	10,706
31	0	48,554	2,000	14,230
32	0	54,381	2,000	18,178
33	0	60,907	2,000	22,599
34	0	68,216	2,000	27,551
35	0	76,802	2,000	33,097
36	0	85,570	2,000	39,309
37	0	95,383	2,000	46,266
38	0	107,339	2,000	54,058
39	0	120,220	2,000	62,785
40	0	134,646	2,000	72,559
41	0	150,804	2,000	83,506
42	0	168,900	2,000	95,767
43	0	189,168	2,000	109,499
44	0	211,869	2,000	124,879
45	0	237,293	2,000	142,104
46	0	265,768	2,000	161,396
47	0	297,660	2,000	183,004
48	0	333,379	2,000	207,204
49	0	373,385	2,000	234,308
50	0	418,191	2,000	264,665
51	0	468,374	2,000	298,665
52	0	524,579	2,000	336,745
53	0	587,528	2,000	379,394
54	0	658,032	2,000	427,161
55	0	736,995	2,000	480,660
56	0	825,435	2,000	540,579
57	0	924,487	2,000	607,688
58	0	1,035,425	2,000	682,851
59	0	1,159,676	2,000	767,033
60	0	1,298,837	2,000	861,317
61	0	1,454,698	2,000	966,915
62	0	1,629,261	2,000	1,085,185
63	0	1,824,773	2,000	1,217,647
64	0	2,043,746	2,000	1,366,005
65	0	***2,288,996***	2,000	***1,532,166***

Saving only $167 a month!

$2,288,996

With only a $16,000 investment!

$1,532,166

Arthur NEVER caught up!

What do we learn from Ben and Arthur?

Rate of return, or ________________ rate, is important.

A simple, one-time investment of $1,000 could make a huge difference at retirement...if you know how and where to invest it.

$1,000 One-Time Investment, No Withdrawal
Age 25 to Age 65 (40 years)

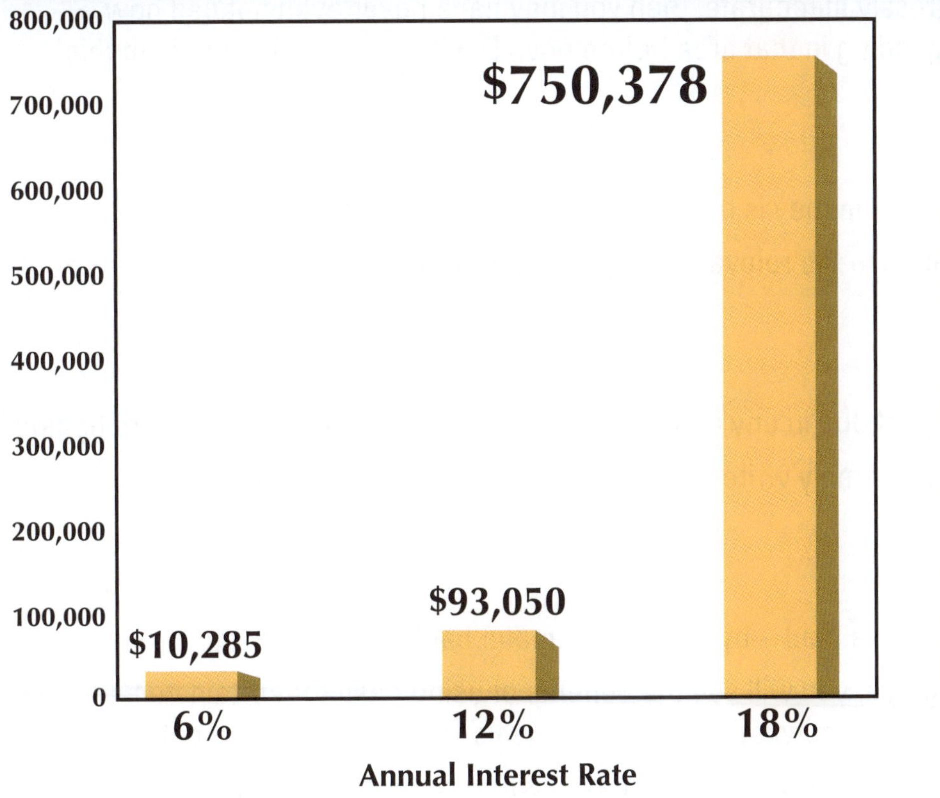

Where you put your money DOES MATTER!

"Make all you can, save all you can, give all you can."

– John Wesley

"Get Rich Quick" never works. You will lose your money. Saving faithfully over time will always build wealth — it just takes a little while.

NOTES

The Basic Quickie Budget (Instructions)

This form will help you get your feet wet in the area of budgeting. It is only one page and should not be intimidating as you get started. The purpose of this form is to show you exactly how much money you need every month in order to survive. We won't get into the details of your credit card bills, student loans, and other consumer debts here. *This is just to give you a starting point as you begin to take control of your money.* You will learn how to create a full monthly cash flow plan in the third class session.

There are four columns on this form:

1. **Monthly Total**
   - This column shows you how much you are spending on necessities each month.
   - If you do not know the amount, write down your best estimate.
   - If an estimate is grossly inaccurate, then you may have never even noticed how much you were spending in that area before now. Don't beat yourself up about this!

2. **Payoff Total**
   - Write down how much money is required to completely pay off that item.
   - This line only appears in the relevant categories (mortgage, car debt, etc.).

3. **How Far Behind?**
   - If your account is past due in any category, write down how many days you are behind.
   - If you are up-to-date, simply write a zero or "N/A" (not applicable) here.

4. **Type of Account**
   - Write in how this area is paid—by check, automatic bank draft, cash, etc.
   - Early in the FPU course, you will see the benefits of using cash for certain items. Challenge yourself by identifying categories for which you can use cash only.
   - The asterisks (*) on the form indicate areas in which a cash-based approach could be helpful.

The Basic Quickie Budget

Item	Monthly Total	Payoff Total	How Far Behind	Type of Account
GIVING	$366		NA	Check
SAVING	$100		NA	Bank Draft
HOUSING				
First Mortgage	$915	$125,000	NA	Bank Draft
Second Mortgage				
Repairs/Mn. Fee				
UTILITIES				
Electricity	$100		NA	Check
Water	$55		NA	Check
Gas	$75		NA	Check
Phone	$45		NA	Check
Trash				
Cable	$21		NA	Check
*Food	$360		NA	Cash
TRANSPORTATION				
Car Payment	$400	$8,500	2 months	Check
Car Payment				
*Gas & Oil	$200		NA	Cash
*Repairs & Tires				
Car Insurance	$80		NA	Check
*CLOTHING	$100		NA	Cash
PERSONAL				
Disability Ins.				
Health Insurance	$300		NA	Bank Draft
Life Insurance				
Child Care				
*Entertainment	$200		NA	Cash
OTHER MISC.				

TOTAL MONTHLY NECESSITIES $3,317

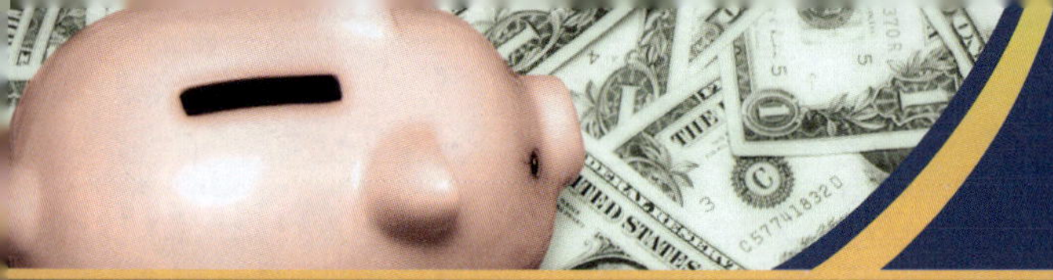

Answer Key

$1,000
$500
Priority
First
Bills
Emotion
Contentment
Amoral
Attitude
Emergency
Fund
Purchases
Wealth
Building
Unexpected

$1,000
3
6
Money
Market
Investment
Insurance
Touch
First
Borrowing
Sinking
$4,000
24%
$211
24

$5,064
$211
18
$464
Discipline
Marathon
Sprint
$100
12%
$1,176,000
Pre-Authorized
Checking
Explosion
Now
Interest

Set Your Goals for the Week / Gazelle Focus

I am going to sit down and do my first Quickie Budget before next week's class.

Also this week, I am going to . . .

Welcome and Introductions

Before starting this week's lesson discussion, get to know the other members in your class. Going around the circle, you should take 1-2 minutes to share:

1. Who you are,
2. Why you're here, and
3. What you hope to get out of this program.

Small Group Discussion and Accountability

Respond to the following discussion questions, sharing openly and giving personal illustrations when possible. Be honest and *real* with each other.

1. What is keeping you from saving?
2. What is Baby Step 1? Why is this important?
3. Why do so many people use debt (credit cards, loans, etc.) for emergencies? Have you ever done this? Be honest!
4. Dave talked about how money is amoral, using the analogy of the brick. What did this illustration mean to you? Have you ever thought of money as being "good" or "bad" in and of itself?
5. What does "Murphy Repellant" mean? If you had some savings built up, do you think you'd have fewer emergencies?
6. Statistics show that most of us will have a major, unexpected, negative financial event in any 10-year period. What would constitute a "negative financial event" in your situation? How would you handle that today?
7. How would it feel if you had savings to cover an emergency? How would that change your attitude when unexpected things happen?

Homework

Get your FPU experience off to a great start by completing these crucial tasks this week:

1. **Complete the Basic Quickie Budget form and *bring this to class next week.*** This is available in the forms section at the back of this workbook or online at daveramsey.com/fpumember.
2. **Register for the Member Resource Center (MRC).** We've packed a ton of useful tools and exclusive benefits into the MRC to enhance your class experience. Visit daveramsey.com/fpumember and start exploring! Be sure to get your class code from your coordinator. You'll need this to gain access to all the extra online resources!
3. ***Financial Peace Revisited*:** Read chapters 1, 2, 3, and 10.

online resources™

Be sure to check out the special online features for this week.

- **Financial Reality Check:** Find out where your current financial plan will lead you!
- **Emergency Fund Tracker:** How fast can you save your first $1,000?
- **Drive Free, Retire Rich:** Discover the best way to buy a car!
- **Private Journal:** Record your progress in your own private journal!

Now that YOU'VE
been empowered...
EMPOWER
YOUR KIDS!
We have tons of resources available
for you AND your kids and teens.
Visit our website at
daveramsey.com
888.22.PEACE

Dave Ramsey's Financial Peace University

Relating With Money™

Nerds and Free Spirits Unite!

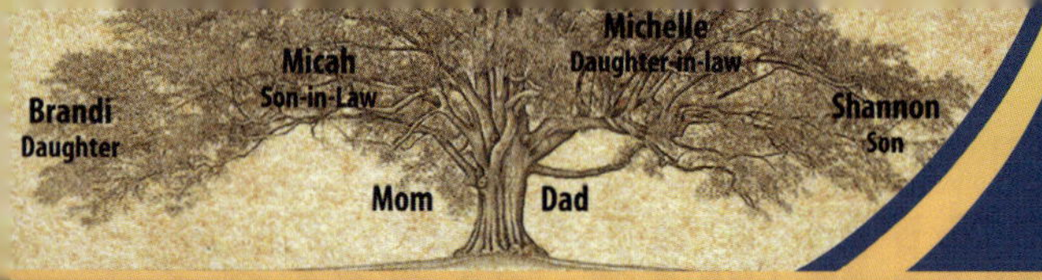

Men, Women, and Money (over-generalizing)

The flow of money in a family represents the ____________ ________________ under which that family operates.

Emergency Fund Savings:

- Men: "It's boring and not ______________________ enough."
- Women: "It's the most __________________ key to our financial plan."

Shopping:

- Men get good deals by ____________________.
- Men want to win.
- Women get good deals by ________________.
- Women enjoy the process.

Financial Problems:

- Men lose _______ - ___________ because money usually represents a _____________________ to them.
- Women face ___________ or even ___________ because, with women, money usually represents ____________.

"The happiest people in the world are those who do the most for others."

– Booker T. Washington

Guys, always be aware of the woman's security gland. When it tightens up, it will affect the whole relationship.

How many marriages would be better if the husband and wife actually understood that they're on the same side?

"Personal relationships are the fertile soil from which all advancement, all success, all achievement in real life grows."

– Ben Stein

Marriage and Money

Can We Talk?

- The number one cause of divorce in America is_____________ _______________.

- When you agree on your value system, you will reach a _________________ in your marriage that you can experience no other way.

Who Does the Financial Decision-Making?

- ____________ of you!

- The partner with the natural ____________ can prepare the ______________, but the decision-making must be done by _____________.

- The _______ likes doing the budget because it gives them control, and they feel like they are taking care of loved ones.

- The _______ ______________ feels controlled, not cared for, and can appear irresponsible to the nerd.

"Therefore a man shall leave his father and mother and be joined to his wife, and they shall become one flesh."

– Genesis 2:24 (NKJV)

"With all lowliness and gentleness, with long-suffering, bearing with one another in love, endeavoring to keep the unity of the Spirit in the bond of peace."

– Ephesians 4:2-3 (NKJV)

online

Keep your Budget Committee Meetings on track! Download and print out a copy of the rules for nerds and free spirits.

NOTES

> Accountability and support are the ladders that lift us up from life's pits.

> "You use steel to sharpen steel, and one friend sharpens another."
>
> –Proverbs 27:17 (The Message)

> "Tell me, and I'll forget. Show me, and I may not remember. Involve me, and I'll understand."
>
> – Native American Saying

> "Criticize the performance, not the performer."
>
> – Anonymous

Singles and Money

- __________ ______________ and fatigue can lead to poor money management.
- Beware of ___________ buying, which can be brought on by ___________ or even by the "I owe it to ________" syndrome.
- A written plan gives the single person _______________, self-accountability, and ___________.

Prevention

- Develop an _______________ relationship.

  This is someone with whom to discuss major __________.

  This is someone with whom to discuss your __________.

- Accountability friends must love you enough to be brutally honest and promise to do so for your own good.

Suggested possibilities: pastoral staff, parent, relative, boss, etc.

Kids and Money

- Teaching your kids how to handle money is not the ________ responsibility. It is ____________ responsibility!

- Pay ________________, not allowance; we have enough people in our society who expect to be made allowance for.

- Words are ______________.

- If you ___________, you get paid; if you do not _________, you do not get paid.

- Teach by ________________.

- Show them how you live ___________ free, how insurance works, how an IRA works, etc.

Be Age-Appropriate

- If the children are young, use a clear ____________ to save. Visual reinforcement is powerful.

- Use three envelopes for ages 5-12: ____________, ____________, and ____________.

- Somewhere around 13-15 years old, open a _____________ _______________ for the child and teach him/her how to run it by monthly reviews.

"Train up a child in the way he should go, and when he is old he will not depart from it. The rich rules over the poor, and the borrower is servant to the lender." – Proverbs 22:6-7 (NKJV)

"But if anyone does not provide for his own, and especially for those of his household, he has denied the faith and is worse than an unbeliever."

– 1 Timothy 5:8 (NKJV)

"Correct your son, and he will give you rest; yes, he will give delight to your soul."

– Proverbs 29:17 (NKJV)

"For even when we were with you, we commanded you this: If anyone will not work, neither shall he eat."

– 2 Thessalonians 3:10 (NKJV)

NOTES

Answer Key

Value
System
Sophisticated
Important
Negotiating
Hunting
Self
Esteem
Scorecard
Fear
Terror
Security
Money
Fights
Unity

Both
Gift
Budget
Both
Nerd
Free Spirit
Time
Poverty
Impulse
Stress
Myself
Empowerment
Control
Accountability
Purchases

Budget
School's
Your
Commissions
Powerful
Work
Work
Example
Debt
Container
Giving
Spending
Saving
Checking
Account

Set Your Goals for the Week / Gazelle Focus

I will Identify an accountability partner this week and give him/her permission to hurt my feelings when necessary for my greater good.

Also this week, I am going to . . .

Review of Last Week

1. Name three reasons why you should save money.
2. What is Baby Step 1? Why is it important to do this first?
3. What can you do to fund your emergency fund quickly?
4. Everyone hold up your completed Basic Quickie Budget form. We told you we'd check to see if you did it!

Class Commitments

1. Make a verbal commitment to start putting something aside for an emergency fund every month, even if it is only $4.
2. Commit to attend all 13 class sessions.

Small Group Discussion and Accountability

1. What are the advantages to being single in regards to financial control? What are the disadvantages?
2. What are some of the reasons that finances should be agreed upon by both partners in a marriage?
3. Do you put relationships above money, making your spouse, children, and friends more important than financial stress? Would others agree with your answer?
4. What are some practical ways to teach your kids about money?
5. Respond to this statement: "How you spend your money tells me who you are and what is important to you."
6. How do fatigue and stress affect your money management?
7. Say aloud: "I did not get into financial stress quickly, and I will most likely walk out of it slowly."

Homework

1. **Start collecting credit card offers.** Keep track of all of the credit card offers that come in the mail throughout the rest of FPU. At the end of the class, we'll total everyone's offers up and see how much potential debt we've avoided in just these 13 weeks!
2. ***Financial Peace Revisited*:** Read chapters 14-18.

online resources™

Be sure to check out the special online features for this week.

- **Learn the Rules:** Download and print a copy of Dave's rules for the "Budget Committee Meeting."
- **Video:** Rachel Ramsey reveals "Five Reasons Why It's So Tough Being Dave Ramsey's Kid"!
- **Junior's Clubhouse:** Dave has a website just for kids! Games, stories, and other resources entertain while teaching important lessons about money.

Dave Ramsey's

Financial Peace® UNIVERSITY

Cash Flow Planning™

The Nuts and Bolts of Budgeting

"Be diligent to know the state of your flocks, and attend to your herds."

– Proverbs 27:23 (NKJV)

"Prepare your outside work, make it fit for yourself in the field; and afterward build your house."

– Proverbs 24:27 (NKJV)

online

Need a refresher on how to balance your checking account?

Check out our free online tutorial today!

Money flows *from* those who don't manage it and *to* those who do.

Budgeting Basics

Money is ________________.

You must do a written __________ ________ plan every month.

You must also keep your checking account _________________.

Overdrafts are a sign of ____________ _____________ and sloppy, lazy money habits.

Use ________________ checks if necessary.

If not managed and made to behave, the ________ card and the __________ card are certain to become budget busters.

- Keep up with your receipts and write them in your account register.
- Use your bank's online tools to keep a close eye on your spending.

Reasons We DON'T Do a Cash Flow Plan

- Most people hate the word "budget" for four reasons:

  1. It has a ____________ _______________ connotation.

  2. It has been used to _________________ them.

  3. They've never had a budget that ________________.

  4. Paralysis from _________________ of what they will find.

- Cash flow plans do not work when you:

  1. _________________ things ___________.

  2. _______________________ your plan.

  3. Don't actually ________ it.

  4. Don't actually ___________ on it.

Most adults are pretty good at budgeting—when they bother to do it on purpose.

Budgeting is not a method by which you make other *people* behave. Budgeting is a method by which you make *money* behave.

"People don't plan to fail, they fail to plan."

– Anonymous

"'Woe to the rebellious children,' says the LORD, 'Who take counsel, but not of Me, and who devise plans, but not of My spirit, that they may add sin to sin.'"

– Isaiah 30:1 (NKJV)

NOTES

Reasons We SHOULD Do a Cash Flow Plan

"The plans of the diligent lead surely to plenty, but those of everyone who is hasty, surely to poverty."
– Proverbs 21:5 (NKJV)

"Commit your works to the LORD, and your thoughts will be established."
– Proverbs 16:3 (NKJV)

"May he give you the desire of your heart and make all your plans succeed."
– Psalm 20:4 (NIV)

- A written plan removes the "management by ____________" from your finances.
- Managed money goes ________________.
- A written plan, if actually lived and agreed on, will remove many of the ________________ ________________ from your marriage.
- A written plan, if actually lived and agreed on, will remove much of the ________________ , ________________, and _____________ that may now be a part of buying necessities such as food or clothing.
- A written plan, if actually lived and agreed on, will remove many of the ________________ from your life, consequently removing a lot of __________.
- A written plan, if actually lived and agreed on, will show if you are ______________________ in a certain area.
- The easiest and most powerful method is a ________- based plan using the _____________ system.

Remember the Four Walls:

1. Food
2. Shelter
3. Clothing
4. Transportation

How To Balance Your Checking Account

- Keep your account register current by subtracting checks, debit card purchases, and withdrawals and adding deposits as they're made to keep your account balanced correctly.

- Balance your checking account within 72 hours of receiving your bank statement or online once a month to make sure there aren't any mistakes.

- What do I need to balance my account?
  1. Your account register
  2. Your last bank statement (in print or online)
  3. A reconciliation sheet (located on the back of most statements)

- Where do I start?

  Start by putting check marks in your register for each of the checks, debit card purchases, and other withdrawals, as well as deposits included in your bank statement. Make an entry in your register for any bank service charges or interest paid.

Checking Account Register

Check Number	Date	Fee	Transaction Description	Payment	Deposit	Balance $564.46
5671	8/12	✗	One Stop Grocery	57.40		507.06
5672	8/14		Electric Company	101.00		406.06
	8/14		Paycheck		700.00	1106.06
5673	8/16		Telephone Company	50.00		1056.06
5674	8/19		One Stop Grocery	66.00		990.06
		✗	Bank Service Charge	2.50		987.56

NOTES

How To Balance Your Checking Account (continued)

- On the reconciliation sheet, list any checks, withdrawals, or other deductions that are in your register that are not on your bank statement and total the list.
- On the reconciliation sheet, list any deposits that are in your register but are not included on your bank statement. Total the list.
- Beginning with the ending balance from your bank statement, subtract the total withdrawals and add the total deposits that were not on your statement.
- Compare with your register balance. If they don't agree, double check your lists and re-add your register entries until you find the difference. If the numbers will not agree, you're probably missing a transaction in your register. Make sure every transaction on your statement has been recorded and try again. In some cases, you may need your bank's help in getting your register to balance if you haven't done it in a while.

List the balance from your bank statement $ 504.56

List the withdrawal amounts in your register that aren't on your statement.

The Electric Company	5672	8/14	101.00
Telephone Company	5673	8/16	50.00
One Stop Grocery	5674	8/19	66.00

TOTAL $ 217.00 (-) $ 217.00

List the deposit amounts in your register that aren't on your statement.

Paycheck	8/14		100.00

TOTAL $ 100.00 (+) $ 100.00

This should be your register balance $ 981.56

Financial Management Forms

Welcome to the wonderful world of cash flow management! This level of detail may seem a bit intimidating at first, but don't worry—we'll walk you through this step by step.

By filling out just a few forms, your new financial plan will start to unfold right in front of you. You'll immediately identify problem areas and learn how to shut the valve of wasteful spending because you'll know exactly where all of your dollars are going!

The first time you fill out these forms, it will take a little while and you'll have to come face-to-face with the bad habits that have gotten you to this point. After that initial start-up, however, you'll get better and better until budgeting becomes second nature.

Complete the whole set of forms to get started. Then, you'll only need to do the "Monthly Cash Flow Plan" (Form 5), "Allocated Spending Plan" (Form 7), or the "Irregular Income Plan" (Form 8) once a month. Dave will teach you which form best fits your specific situation. This should only take about 30 minutes a month once you get in the habit.

You'll also want to update the whole set of forms once a year or whenever you experience a dramatic positive or negative financial event (such as receiving a large inheritance or paying for a major house repair).

Are you ready? It's time to make those dollars dance! Go for it!

Sample forms are provided here. The actual blank forms for you to use are found in the forms section at the back of this book.

online

All of these forms are also available for download. You can even do your monthly budget online with our powerful Gazelle Budget Software—FREE during your FPU class.

NOTES

Major Components of a Healthy Financial Plan (Form 1)

	Action Needed	Action Date
Written Cash Flow Plan	Complete first budget	NOW!
Will and/or Estate Plan	Make an appt. with lawyer	June 6
Debt Reduction Plan	Begin debt snowball	July 1
Tax Reduction Plan	NA	NA
Emergency Funding	On hold until Baby Step 3	NA
Retirement Funding	On hold until Baby Step 4	NA
College Funding	On hold until Baby Step 5	NA
Charitable Giving	Start tithing	June 15
Teach My Children	Get Financial Peace Jr.	August
Life Insurance	Done	NA
Health Insurance	Done	NA
Disability Insurance	Check company options	This week
Auto Insurance	Check current policy details	July 1
Homeowner's Insurance	Check replacement cost	This week

I (We) Joe & Suzie Public, (a) responsible adult(s), do hereby promise to take the above stated actions by the above stated dates to financially secure the well-being of my (our) family and myself (ourselves).

Signed: Joe Q. Public Date: June 2

Signed: Suzie Q. Public Date: June 2

Consumer Equity Sheet (Form 2)

ITEM / DESCRIBE	VALUE	–	DEBT	=	EQUITY
Real Estate ______	$180,000		$149,000		$31,000
Real Estate ______					
Car ______	$2,500				$2,500
Car ______	$3,000				$3,000
Cash On Hand					
Checking Account					
Checking Account					
Savings Account	$1,600				$1,600
Money Market Account					
Mutual Funds					
Retirement Plan 1	$400				$400
Retirement Plan 2	$8,000				$8,000
Cash Value (Insurance)					
Household Items	$30,000				$30,000
Jewelry					
Antiques					
Boat					
Unsecured Debt (Neg)					
Credit Card Debt (Neg)					
Other ______					
Other ______					
Other ______					
TOTAL	$225,500		$149,000		$76,500

Income Sources (Form 3)

SOURCE	AMOUNT	PERIOD/DESCRIBE
Salary 1	$2,716	1st of Month
Salary 2	$945	1st & 15th - $472.50
Salary 3		
Bonus		
Self-Employment		
Interest Income		
Dividend Income		
Royalty Income		
Rents		
Notes		
Alimony		
Child Support		
AFDC		
Unemployment		
Social Security		
Pension		
Annuity		
Disability Income		
Cash Gifts		
Trust Fund		
Other_______		
Other_______		
Other_______		
TOTAL	$3,661	

Lump Sum Payment Planning (Form 4)

Payments you make on a non-monthly basis, such as insurance premiums and taxes, can be budget busters if you do not plan for them every month. Therefore, you must annualize the cost and convert these to monthly budget items. That way, you can save the money each month and will not be caught off-guard when your bi-monthly, quarterly, semi-annual, or annual bills come due. Simply divide the annual cost by 12 to determine the monthly amount you should save for each item.

ITEM NEEDED	ANNUAL AMOUNT		MONTHLY AMOUNT
Real Estate Taxes	______	/ 12 =	______
Homeowner's Insurance	______	/ 12 =	______
Home Repairs	$1,800	/ 12 =	$150
Replace Furniture	______	/ 12 =	______
Medical Bills	$600	/ 12 =	$50
Health Insurance	______	/ 12 =	______
Life Insurance	______	/ 12 =	______
Disability Insurance	______	/ 12 =	______
Car Insurance	______	/ 12 =	______
Car Repair/Tags	______	/ 12 =	______
Replace Car	______	/ 12 =	______
Clothing	______	/ 12 =	______
Tuition	______	/ 12 =	______
Bank Note	______	/ 12 =	______
IRS (Self-Employed)	______	/ 12 =	______
Vacation	$1,200	/ 12 =	$100
Gifts (including Christmas)	______	/ 12 =	______
Other ______	______	/ 12 =	______

Monthly Cash Flow Plan (Instructions)

Every single dollar of your income should be allocated to some category on this form. When you're done, your total income minus expenses should equal zero. If it doesn't, then you need to adjust some categories (such as debt reduction, giving, or saving) so that it does equal zero. Use some common sense here, too. Do not leave things like clothes, car repairs, or home improvements off this list. If you don't plan for these things, then you're only setting yourself up for failure later.

Yes, this budget form is long. It's *really* long. We do that so that we can list practically every expense imaginable on this form to prevent you from forgetting something. Don't expect to put something on *every* line item. Just use the ones that are relevant to your specific situation.

Every main category on this form has subcategories. Fill in the monthly expense for each subcategory, and then write down the grand total for that category. Later, as you actually pay the bills and work through the month, use the "Actually Spent" column to record what you really spent in each area. If there is a substantial difference between what you budgeted and what you spent, then you'll need to readjust the budget to make up for the difference. If one category continually comes up over or short for two or three months, then you need to adjust the budgeted amount accordingly.

Use the "% Take Home Pay" column to record what percentage of your income actually goes to each category. Then, use the "Recommended Percentages" sheet (Form 6) to see if your percentages are in line with what we recommend.

Notes:

- An asterisk (*) beside an item indicates an area for which you should use the envelope system.
- The emergency fund should get all the savings until you've completed your full emergency fund of three to six months of expenses (Baby Step 3).
- Don't forget to include your annualized items from the "Lump Sum Payment Planning" sheet (Form 4), including your Christmas gift planning.

Monthly Cash Flow Plan (Form 5)

Budgeted Item	Sub Total	TOTAL	Actually Spent	% of Take Home Pay
CHARITABLE GIFTS		$366		10%
SAVING				
Emergency Fund	$224			
Retirement Fund				
College Fund		$224		6%
HOUSING				
First Mortgage	$915			
Second Mortgage				
Real Estate Taxes				
Homeowner's Ins.				
Repairs or Mn. Fee				
Replace Furniture	$50			
Other ________		$965		27%
UTILITIES				
Electricity	$100			
Water	$55			
Gas	$75			
Phone	$45			
Trash				
Cable	$21	$296		8%
*FOOD				
*Grocery	$360			
*Restaurants	$50	$410		12%
TRANSPORTATION				
Car Payment				
Car Payment				
*Gas and Oil	$150			
*Repairs and Tires				
Car Insurance	$80			
License and Taxes				
Car Replacement		$230		5%
PAGE 1 TOTAL		$2,491		

Monthly Cash Flow Plan (Form 5 – continued)

Budgeted Item	Sub Total	TOTAL	Actually Spent	% of Take Home Pay
*CLOTHING				
*Children				
*Adults	$100			
*Cleaning/Laundry		$100		3%
MEDICAL/HEALTH				
Disability Insurance				
Health Insurance	$300			
Doctor Bills	$50			
Dentist	$20			
Optometrist				
Medications		$370		10%
PERSONAL				
Life Insurance	$65			
Child Care				
*Baby Sitter				
*Toiletries				
*Cosmetics				
*Hair Care	$60			
Education/Adult				
School Tuition				
School Supplies				
Child Support				
Alimony				
Subscriptions				
Organization Dues	$25			
Gifts (incl. Christmas)				
Miscellaneous	$50			
*Blow Money	$100	$300		8%
PAGE 2 TOTAL		$770		

Monthly Cash Flow Plan (Form 5 – continued)

Budgeted Item	Sub Total	TOTAL	Actually Spent	% of Take Home Pay
RECREATION				
*Entertainment	$50			
Vacation	$25	$75		2%
DEBTS (Hopefully -0-)				
Visa 1	$100			
Visa 2				
Master Card 1	$75			
Master Card 2				
American Express	$50			
Discover Card				
Gas Card 1				
Gas Card 2				
Dept. Store Card 1				
Dept. Store Card 2				
Finance Co. 1				
Finance Co. 2				
Credit Line				
Student Loan 1	$100			
Student Loan 2				
Other ________				
Other ________				
Other ________				
Other ________				
Other ________		$325		9%
PAGE 3 TOTAL		$400		
PAGE 2 TOTAL		$770		
PAGE 1 TOTAL		$2,491		
GRAND TOTAL		$3661		
TOTAL HOUSEHOLD INCOME		$3661		
		ZERO		

Recommended Percentages (Form 6)

How much of your income should be spent on housing, giving, food, etc.? Through experience and research, we recommend the following percentages. However, you should remember that these are only *recommended* percentages. If you have an unusually high or low income, then these numbers could change dramatically. For example, if you have a high income, the *percentage* that is spent on food will be much lower than someone who earns half of that.

If you find that you spend much more in one category than we recommend, however, it may be necessary to adjust your lifestyle in that area in order to enjoy more freedom and flexibility across the board.

ITEM	ACTUAL %	RECOMMENDED %
CHARITABLE GIFTS	10%	10 – 15%
SAVING	6%	5 – 10%
HOUSING	27%	25 – 35%
UTILITIES	8%	5 – 10%
FOOD	12%	5 – 15%
TRANSPORTATION	5%	10 – 15%
CLOTHING	3%	2 – 7%
MEDICAL/HEALTH	10%	5 – 10%
PERSONAL	8%	5 – 10%
RECREATION	2%	5 – 10%
DEBTS	9%	5 – 10%

Allocated Spending Plan (Instructions)

Now that you've already planned out the entire month on the "Monthly Cash Flow Plan" (Form 5), let's get just a little bit more precise. On this form, you will allocate—or spend—all of your money from each individual pay period.

There are four columns on this form, representing the four weeks in a given month. You will use one column for each week you get paid. If you are married and your spouse earns an income, then you will both use this same form. For weeks in which you both receive a paycheck, simply add those two incomes together and use a single column. Be sure to write the pay date at the top of the column.

Now, go down the list and allocate each expense to a specific payday, using your bills' due dates as a guide. For example, if your phone bill is due on the 22nd and you get paid on the 15th and 30th, then you know that you would probably pay that bill from your income on the 15th. Some things, like utility bills, will be paid monthly, while other items, such as food and gasoline, could be weekly. The point here is to anticipate both your upcoming expenses and your upcoming income and plan accordingly.

Beside each line item, you'll see two blanks separated by a slash (/). Put the expense to the left of the slash and the remaining income from that pay period to the right of the slash. As you work your way down the column, the income remaining should diminish until you reach a perfect zero at the bottom of the list. If you have money left over at the end of the column, go back and adjust an area, such as savings or giving, so that you spend every single dollar.

This level of detail may be uncomfortable to you at first, but the payoff is worth it. By specifically "naming" every dollar before you actually get it in your hands, you will remove an incredible amount of stress and curb your overspending.

NOTES:

- If you have an irregular income, such as self-employment or commissions, you should use the "Irregular Income Planning" sheet (Form 8) instead of this "Allocated Spending Plan."
- If you know that you have an impulse spending problem, then you may want to allocate more money to the "Blow" category. That way, you are at least planning for it and setting up some boundaries for yourself.
- An asterisk (*) beside an item indicates an area for which you should use the envelope system.

Allocated Spending Plan (Form 7)

ITEM:	PAY PERIOD: 1 / 1	1 / 8	1 / 15	1 / 22
INCOME	$3,188	0	$472	0
CHARITABLE	366 / 2822	/	/	/
SAVING				
Emergency Fund	224 / 2598	/	/	/
Retirement Fund	/	/	/	/
College Fund	/	/	/	/
HOUSING				
First Mortgage	915 / 1683	/	/	/
Second Mortgage	/	/	/	/
Real Estate Taxes	/	/	/	/
Homeowner's Ins.	/	/	/	/
Repairs or Mn. Fees	/	/	/	/
Replace Furniture	/	/	50 / 422	/
Other _______	/	/	/	/
UTILITIES				
Electricity	100 / 1583	/	/	/
Water	/	/	55 / 367	/
Gas	/	/	75 / 292	/
Phone	45 / 1538	/	/	/
Trash	/	/	/	/
Cable	21 / 1517	/	/	/
*FOOD				
*Grocery	200 / 1317	/	160 / 132	/
*Restaurants	25 / 1292	/	25 / 107	/

Allocated Spending Plan (Form 7 – continued)

TRANSPORTATION				
Car Payment	/	/	/	/
Car Payment	/	/	/	/
*Gas and Oil	75 / 1217	/	75 / 32	/
*Repairs and Tires	/	/	/	/
Car Insurance	80 / 1137	/	/	/
License and Taxes	/	/	/	/
Car Replacement	/	/	/	/
*CLOTHING				
*Children	/	/	/	/
*Adults	100 / 1037	/	/	/
*Cleaning/Laundry	/	/	/	/
MEDICAL/HEALTH				
Disability Insurance	/	/	/	/
Health Insurance	300 / 737	/	/	/
Doctor	50 / 687	/	/	/
Dentist	/	/	20 / 12	/
Optometrist	/	/	/	/
Medications	/	/	/	/
PERSONAL				
Life Insurance	65 / 622	/	/	/
Child Care	/	/	/	/
*Baby Sitter	/	/	/	/
*Toiletries	/	/	/	/
*Cosmetics	/	/	/	/
*Hair Care	/	/	/	/
Education/Adult	60 / 562	/	/	/
School Tuition	/	/	/	/
School Supplies	/	/	/	/
Child Support	/	/	/	/

Allocated Spending Plan (Form 7 – continued)

Alimony	/	/	/	/
Subscriptions	/	/	/	/
Organization Dues	25 / 537	/	/	/
Gifts (including Christmas)	/	/	/	/
Miscellaneous	50 / 487	/	/	/
*BLOW $$	100 / 387	/	/	/
RECREATION				
*Entertainment	50 / 337	/	/	/
Vacation	25 / 312	/	/	/
DEBTS (Hopefully -0-)				
Visa 1	100 / 212	/	/	/
Visa 2	/	/	/	/
MasterCard 1	75 / 137	/	/	/
MasterCard 2	/	/	/	/
American Express	50 / 87	/	/	/
Discover Card	/	/	/	/
Gas Card 1	/	/	/	/
Gas Card 2	/	/	/	/
Dept. Store Card 1	/	/	/	/
Dept. Store Card 2	/	/	/	/
Finance Co. 1	/	/	/	/
Finance Co. 2	/	/	/	/
Credit Line	/	/	/	/
Student Loan 1	87 / 0	/	12 / 0	/
Student Loan 2	/	/	/	/
Other ________	/	/	/	/
Other ________	/	/	/	/

Irregular Income Planning (Form 8)

Many people have an "irregular" income, which simply means that their compensation fluctuates from month to month. This is especially common for the self-employed, as well as commission-based salespeople. While this makes it more difficult to predict your income, you are still responsible for doing a monthly budget!

The "Monthly Cash Flow Plan" (Form 5) should remain a crucial part of your plan, as it lays out exactly how much money you need to bring home each month to survive and prosper. However, instead of doing the "Allocated Spending Plan" (Form 7), you will use this "Irregular Income Planning" sheet.

On this form, simply look at the individual items from your "Monthly Cash Flow Plan" sheet and prioritize them by importance. Ask yourself, "If I only have enough money to pay one thing, what would that be?" Put that at the top of your list. Then, ask yourself, "If I only have enough money to pay one more thing, what would that be?" That's number two. Keep this up all the way down the list.

With your list in place, you're ready to get paid. If you get a $1,500 paycheck, you will spend that $1,500 right down the list until it is gone, recording the cumulative amount spent in the "Cumulative Amount" column. At that point, you're finished spending, no matter what remains unpaid on the list. That's why the most important things are at the top of the list, right?

Be prepared to stand your ground. Things usually have a way of seeming *important* when they are only *urgent*. For example, a once-in-a-lifetime opportunity to see your favorite band perform live may seem *important*, but in reality, it is only *urgent*, meaning that it is time-sensitive. Urgency alone should not move an item to the top of this list!

Item	Amount	Cumulative Amount
JC Penney	$150	$150
Sears	$250	$400
Visa	$500	$900
Vacation - part	$200	$1100
Christmas	$400	$1500

Breakdown of Savings (Form 9)

After you have fully funded your emergency fund, you can start to save for other items, such as furniture, car replacement, home maintenance, or a vacation. This sheet will remind you that every dollar in your savings account is already committed to something. For example, it's a bad idea to take money away from car repairs to pay for an impulse Hawaiian vacation, even if you pay cash for it. What would you do if the car broke down the week you got back home? However, it can be okay to reassign the dollars to another category, as long as you do it on purpose and it doesn't put you in a pinch in another category. Keep up with your breakdown of savings every month, one quarter at a time.

Item		Balance By Month		
		October	November	December
Emergency Fund (1)	$1,000			
Emergency Fund (2)	3-6 months			
Retirement Fund				
College Fund				
Real Estate Taxes				
Homeowner's Insurance				
Repairs or Mn. Fee				
Replace Furniture				
Car Insurance				
Car Replacement		$600	$700	$800
Disability Insurance				
Health Insurance		$500	$500	$500
Doctor				
Dentist				
Optometrist				
Life Insurance				
School Tuition				
School Supplies				
Gifts (incl. Christmas)		$500	$650	$800
Vacation				
Other ____________				
Other ____________				
TOTAL		$1,600	$1,850	$2,100

Financial Snapshot

Please complete the first column of the Financial Snapshot immediately following Session 3.

FINANCIAL SNAPSHOT

FINANCIAL PEACE UNIVERSITY EST·1994

CLASS START DATE (MM/DD/YY) ___/___/___

CLASS LOCATION CODE

FIRST NAME

SPOUSE FIRST NAME

LAST NAME

Complete this form online at daveramsey.com/fpumember

COORDINATOR FIRST NAME

COORDINATOR LAST NAME

Complete information in column 1, session #3, based upon your current financial situation since you started applying the "Financial Peace" principles; even if you started applying them prior to taking the FPU class.

Areas to work on IMMEDIATELY	Session 3	Session 6	Session 9	Session 12
Have a budget that works?	O Yes O No	O Yes O No	O Yes O No	O Yes O No
Paying necessities before creditors?	O Yes O No	O Yes O No	O Yes O No	O Yes O No
Cut up all credit cards?	O Yes O No	O Yes O No	O Yes O No	O Yes O No
Living on envelope system?	O Yes O No	O Yes O No	O Yes O No	O Yes O No
How many envelopes?				
$1000 in emergency fund?	O Yes O No	O Yes O No	O Yes O No	O Yes O No
Amount now in fund?	$	$	$	$
Giving to worthy causes?	O Yes O No	O Yes O No	O Yes O No	O Yes O No
Using the buddy system?	O Yes O No	O Yes O No	O Yes O No	O Yes O No
Debts paid?	O Yes O No	O Yes O No	O Yes O No	O Yes O No
How much $$ so far?	$	$	$	$
3-6 months expenses saved?	O Yes O No	O Yes O No	O Yes O No	O Yes O No
How many months saved?				
Saving now for major purchases?	O Yes O No	O Yes O No	O Yes O No	O Yes O No
List types.				
Funding pre-tax savings?	O Yes O No	O Yes O No	O Yes O No	O Yes O No
College funding started?	O Yes O No	O Yes O No	O Yes O No	O Yes O No
Paying extra on mortgages?	O Yes O No	O Yes O No	O Yes O No	O Yes O No
Walking in Financial Peace?	O Yes O No	O Yes O No	O Yes O No	O Yes O No

46094

online

You can also easily complete your ***Financial Snapshot*** online!

Be sure to visit daveramsey.com/fpumember for more information!

NOTES

Answer Key

Active
Cash
Flow
Balanced
Crisis
Living
Duplicate
ATM
Debit
Straight
Jacket
Abuse

Worked
Fear
Leave
Out
Overcomplicate
Do
Live
Crisis
Farther
Money
Fights
Guilt

Shame
Fear
Overdrafts
Stress
Overspending
Zero
Envelope

Set Your Goals for the Week / Gazelle Focus

Before the next class, I/we will complete my/our first full cash flow plan.

Also this week, I am going to . . .

Review of Last Week

1. The flow of money represents your family's:
   A. Income B. Value System C. Teamwork
2. Explain the concept of the Nerd and Free Spirit.
3. Who should do the financial decision-making in a marriage?
4. How can an accountability partner help a single person win with money?

Small Group Discussion and Accountability

1. What are the benefits of a written cash flow plan? Be specific. How can this impact a marriage? How can it strengthen a single person?
2. What things have kept you from living on a cash flow plan?
3. What are some reasons why you've always hated the idea of a budget? What are your initial reactions to the concept?
4. How can the concept of the Four Walls (food, shelter, clothing, transportation) empower you to prioritize your spending?
5. When have you been guilty of letting someone else set your family's financial priorities? Explain.
6. How well do you understand the cash envelope system? In what areas of your budget could you implement this immediately?
7. Why is it important to set aside a little "blow money" every month?

Homework

1. **Complete your first Financial Snapshot,** either online or on the paper form that came with your workbook.
2. **Create a full zero-based budget for your household this week,** using either the Monthly Cash Flow Plan form or the online budgeting software. ***Remember to bring your budget to next week's class session!***
3. ***Financial Peace Revisited*:** Read chapters 19 and 21.

online resources™

Be sure to check out the special online features for this week.

- **Financial Snapshot:** Track your progress with this quick online form.
- **Gazelle Budget Software:** Create and maintain your budget with our exclusive online software!
- **Budget Forms:** Download printable copies of all the forms discussed in this lesson.
- **Checkbook Help:** Get a quick refresher on how to balance your checking account!
- **Free Podcast:** Get a daily dose of Dave!

Bring A Friend!

FPU is for everyone from the financially secure to the financially distressed.

Be sure to invite a friend or loved one to attend one class session for free as our guest!

Dave Ramsey's Financial Peace® UNIVERSITY

Dumping Debt™

Breaking the Chains of Debt

Debunking the Myth

If you tell a lie or spread a __________ often enough, loud enough, and long enough, the myth becomes accepted as _____________.

Debt has been _______________ to us in so many forms and so aggressively since the 1960s that to even imagine living without it requires a complete __________________ _______.

Myth: If I loan money to a friend or relative, I will be ______________ them.

Truth: The relationship will be strained or _______________.

Myth: By _________________ a loan, I am helping out a friend or relative.

Truth: The bank requires a cosigner because the person isn't likely to __________. So, be ready to pay the loan and have your credit damaged because you are on the loan.

"The rich rules over the poor, and the borrower is servant to the lender."

– Proverbs 22:7 (NKJV)

Quick History of Plastic:

- The credit card was born in 1950.
- The Bank Americard and American Express were created in 1958.
- The VISA brand was established in 1976.
- Discover entered the scene in 1986.

"It's stupid to guarantee someone else's loan."

– Proverbs 17:18 (CEV)

Myth: Cash advance, rent-to-own, title pawning, and tote-the-note car lots are needed ______________ for lower income people to get ahead.

Truth: These are horrible, ____________ rip-offs that aren't needed and benefit no one but the owners of these companies.

Myth: Playing the lottery and other forms of gambling will make me ___________.

Truth: The lottery is a tax on the poor and on people who can't do _____________.

Myth: Car _______________ are a way of life, and you'll always have one.

Truth: Staying away from car payments by driving reliable used cars is what the typical millionaire does. That is ________ they became millionaires.

If you do rich people stuff, you get rich.

If you do poor people stuff, you get poor.

It's really that simple.

"Owe no one anything except to love one another."

– Romans 13:8 (NKJV)

NOTES

Find out the truth about how much that brand new car really costs you in the long run.

Check out ***"Drive Free, Retire Rich"*** in this lesson's online resources.

Myth: ____________ your car is what sophisticated financial people do. You should always lease things that go down in value. There are tax advantages.

Truth: *Consumer Reports, Smart Money* magazine, and a good calculator will tell you that the car lease is the most _______________ way to finance and operate a vehicle.

Truth: If you own a business, you can write off your ________ car on taxes without paying payments for the privilege.

Truth: The way to minimize the money lost on things that go down in value is to buy slightly _________.

Myth: You can get a good deal on a _______ car.

Truth: A new car loses _____% of its value in the first four years. This is the largest purchase most consumers make that goes down in value.

Myth: I'll take out a 30-year mortgage and pay ________, I promise!

Truth: Life happens! Something else will always seem more important, so almost no one pays extra every month. Never take more than a __________ fixed-rate loan.

30 Year vs. 15 Year Mortgage at 6%

		PAYMENT	TOTAL	PAY BACK
Home Purchased	$250,000	30 years	$1,349	$485,636
Down Payment	$ 25,000	15 years	$1,899	$341,762
Mortgage Amount	$225,000	Difference	$ 550	$143,874

You Save More Than $143,000!

Myth: It is wise to take out an _________ or a ______________ mortgage if "I know I'll be moving."

Truth: You *will* be moving when they __________________.

NOTES

"If you want to get yourself better off financially, QUIT BUYING THINGS!"

– Anonymous

Myth: You need a credit card to ____________ a car or to make ____________ online or by phone.

Truth: A ____________ card will do all of that, except for a few major rental companies. Check in advance.

Myth: "I pay mine off every ____________ with no annual fee. I get brownie points, air miles, and a free hat."

Truth: A recent Dun and Bradstreet study found that when you use plastic instead of cash, you spend ____________% more because spending cash hurts. So what if you get 1% back and a free hat?

Myth: I'll make sure my ________________ gets a credit card so he/she can learn to be responsible with money.

Truth: Teens are a huge ____________ of credit card companies today.

Myth: The home equity loan is good for ________________ and is a substitute for an emergency fund.

Truth: You don't go into ________ for emergencies.

Myth: Debt consolidation ________ interest, and you get just one smaller payment.

Truth: Debt consolidation is a _________.

Truth: Debt consolidation typically saves __________ or ______ interest because you will throw your low interest loans into the deal.

Truth: You can't ____________ your way out of debt.

Truth: Smaller payments equal more _______ in debt.

"My son, if you have become surety for your friend, if you have shaken hands in pledge for a stranger, you are snared by the words of your mouth; you are taken by the words of your mouth.

So do this, my son, and deliver yourself; for you have come into the hand of your friend: go and humble yourself; plead with your friend.

Give no sleep to your eyes, nor slumber to your eyelids.

Deliver yourself like a gazelle from the hand of the hunter, and like a bird from the hand of the fowler."

– Proverbs 6:1-5 (NKJV)

NOTES

Myth: Debt is a _______ and should be used to create prosperity.

Truth: The borrower is ________ to the lender.

Truth: When surveyed, the Forbes 400 were asked, "What is the most important key to building wealth?" _______% replied that becoming and staying debt free was the number one key to wealth building.

How much could you __________, invest, blow, and _________ if you had no payments?

Steps Out of Debt

1. Quit ___________________ more ____________________!
2. You must ___________________ money.
3. _______________________ really works.
4. ________ something.
5. Take a part-time _________ or ______________ (temporarily).

Baby Step 2™

Pay off all debt using the _____________ ______________.

Credit Card Crumbs

- The total American consumer debt is more than $2.7 trillion.
- The average household credit card debt has increased approximately 167% in the past 17 years.
- There are over 1.3 billion credit cards in circulation in America.
- The credit card industry mails out over six billion credit card offers each year, sending an average of six offers a month to each American household.
- 45% of American cardholders make only the minimum payments on their consumer debt.
- The average balance per credit card-holding household is more than $9,300.
- It would take over 13 years to pay off the average credit card balance if only making minimum monthly payments of 4% at an average interest rate of 15%.
- Credit card interest rates are often raised when a cardholder takes out a new loan, such as a mortgage, car loan, or other type of credit account.
- A single, first offense late payment can immediately raise a cardholder's interest rate as high as 34%. A "late payment" is defined as anything that posts after 2:00 p.m. on the due date.
- In addition to increasing the cardholder's interest rate, a card issuer can charge a fee of typically $29-39 for a late payment.
- The credit card industry takes in $43 billion per year in additional, unexpected fees from the consumer, such as late payment, over-the-limit, and balance transfer fees. Late fees alone bring in more than $11 billion.
- Overall, American households spend over $412 billion in credit card charges each year.

NOTES

Debt Snowball (Instructions)

Now it's time to knock out that debt! List your debts in order, from the smallest balance to the largest. Don't be concerned with interest rates, unless two debts have a similar payoff balance. In that case, list the one with the higher interest rate first. As you start eliminating debts, you'll start to build some serious momentum. These quick wins will keep you motivated, so you'll be able to stay on track.

The idea of the snowball is simple: pay minimum payments on all of your debts except for the smallest one. Then, attack that one with gazelle intensity! Every extra dollar you can get your hands on should be thrown at that smallest debt until it is gone. Then, you attack the second one. Every time you pay a debt off, you add its old minimum payment to your next debt payments. So, as the snowball rolls over, it picks up more snow. Get it?

Redo this sheet every time you pay off a debt so that you can see how close you're getting to total debt freedom. Keep the old sheets for encouragement—or to wallpaper the bathroom in your debt-free house someday!

The "New Payment" is the total of the previous debt's payment PLUS the current debt's minimum. As these payments compound, you'll start making huge payments as you work down the list. To factor in interest rates and calculate the exact date you will become DEBT FREE, use our online debt snowball tool at daveramsey.com/fpumember (available throughout your 13-week FPU class).

Debt Snowball (Form 10)

Item	Total Payoff	Minimum Payment	New Payment
JC Penney	$150	$15	(Garage Sale)
Sears	$250	$10	$25
Visa	$500	$75	$100
MasterCard	$1,500	$90	$190
Car	$4,000	$210	$400
Student Loan	$4,000	$65	$465

Answer Key

Myth
Truth
Marketed
Paradigm
Shift
Helping
Destroyed
Co-signing
Repay
Services
Greedy
Rich
Math
Payments

How
Leasing
Expensive
Paid-For
Used
New
70%
Extra
15-Year
ARM
Balloon
Foreclose
Rent
Purchases

Debit
Month
12-18%
Teenager
Target
Consolidation
Debt
Saves
Con
Little
No
Borrow
Time
Tool

Slave
75%
Save
Give
Borrowing
Money
Save
Prayer
Sell
Job
Overtime
Debt
Snowball

Set Your Goals for the Week / Gazelle Focus

I am going to complete Baby Step 1 and move on to my Debt Snowball by this date:

Also this week, I am going to . . .

Review of Last Week

1. What is a zero-based budget? Why is it important?
2. Name one of the three reasons we need to do a zero-based budget each month.
3. Hold your budget up! How did your first family budget session go?

Small Group Discussion and Accountability

1. How old were you when you got your first credit card? How did that make you feel (at the time)?
2. What would it feel like to have absolutely no debt?
3. Think about all the money that is currently going out in the form of debt payments (credit cards, furniture, car loan, mortgage, etc.). What could you do with all that money every month if you actually got to keep it?
4. Do you currently have or have you ever had a debt CONsolidation loan? Did you discover that it really was a con?
5. Have you ever believed or spread any of the myths covered in this lesson? Which ones?
6. Why is "gazelle intensity" so important in getting out of debt?
7. What is your reaction to the phrase, "the borrower is *slave* to the lender"?
8. Do you have any questions about the debt snowball?

Homework

1. **Complete the Credit Card History form** and use it as a guide as you start to close those accounts as soon as possible.
2. **Complete your Debt Snowball form** and get ready to dump your debt! ***Bring this form to next week's class.*** Use the Debt Snowball form or the Debt Snowball tool online.
3. ***Financial Peace Revisited*:** Read chapters 7 and 8.

online resources™

Be sure to check out the special online features for this week.

- **Debt Snowball Software:** Track your progress and calculate your DEBT FREE date!
- **Drive Free, Retire Rich:** Discover the best way to buy a car.

FINANCIAL PEACE UNIVERSITY
GUARANTEE

If you do it, it works.
If you don't do it, it won't work!

If you *will* work the program,
you *won't want* your money back.

If you *don't* work the program,
you *don't get* your money back!

Dave Ramsey's
Financial Peace
UNIVERSITY

Dave Ramsey's Financial Peace University

Credit Sharks In Suits™

Understanding Credit Bureaus & Collection Practices

Credit Score

One more myth...

Myth: You need to take out a credit card or car loan to "build up your __________ ______________."

Truth: The FICO score is an "I love __________" score and is not a measure of _____________ financially.

Credit Bureaus

Account information is removed from your credit report ______ years after the last activity on that account, except for a Chapter 7 bankruptcy, which stays on for ________ years.

Beware of credit clean-up scams. The only information that may be legally removed from a credit report is _____________ information.

The National Association of State Public Interest Research Groups (U.S. PIRG) did a survey of 200 adults in 30 states who checked their credit report for accuracy.

- ______% of those credit reports contained mistakes of some kind and ______% of them contained errors serious enough to result in the denial of credit.

With a 20% down payment on a reasonable house, two years or more on the job, and two years of paying your landlord early, you will qualify for a mortgage.

Don't fall for the lie!

FICO stands for Fair Isaac Corporation, which developed a score-based rating system that many companies use to measure an individual's credit risk.

While this measurement has become widely accepted, it is a faulty standard that is based on debt, not wealth.

- _______% of the credit reports contained credit accounts that had been closed by the consumer but incorrectly remained listed as open.

- _______% listed the same mortgage or loan twice.

You should check your credit report _______________, which you can now do for free.

Identity Theft

What To Do:

1. Place a ___________ _________________ alert on your credit bureau report (stays on for 90 days without a police report).

2. Get a ______________ _______________.

3. Remember, this is ________________. You owe _____________ and should pay _________________.

4. Contact the fraud victim ____________________ of each creditor and furnish __________________________.

5. Be _________________________ — this will take some time. You now have a new ______________.

Learn how to check your credit report online for free in this lesson's online resources.

Of all the identity theft victims who call in to *The Dave Ramsey Show* for help and advice on this subject, approximately one-half know the person who stole their identities. The thief is often a friend or a family member.

NOTES

Correcting Credit Report Inaccuracies

"Victory belongs to the most persevering."

– Napoleon

An updated version of the 1977 Federal Fair Credit Reporting Act requires a credit bureau to _______________ all inaccuracies within 30 days of notification of such inaccuracies.

To clean your credit report of inaccurate information, you should write a separate letter for each inaccuracy, staple a copy of your credit report to each letter, and circle the account number.

Note: You should also request that "inquiries" be removed. All of these letters should be sent ____________ mail with return receipt requested to prove when they receive the letter. If the credit bureau does not prove the accuracy of the account within 30 days, you should request they remove the ____________ account from your file.

You will have to be assertive after the 30-day period.

Lodge any _______________ with the Federal Trade Commission and your state's Consumer Affairs Division.

Collection Practices

- The best way to pay debts is with a __________.
- A collector's job is not to help your overall situation. His only job is to get your ______________.
- Collectors are trained ________________ or ___________________.
- They are typically low-paid positions with high __________.
- They are taught in their training to evoke strong __________.
- The way to counteract this technique is to ALWAYS pay ________________ first, and then ________ set the order of payment.

"Many are the plans in a man's heart, but it is the LORD's purpose that prevails."

– Proverbs 19:21 (NIV)

"There is no dignity quite so impressive, and no independence quite so important, as living within your means."

– Calvin Coolidge

NOTES

Federal Fair Debt Collection Practices Act

In 1977, a consumer law was passed by Congress called the Federal Fair Debt Collection Practices Act to protect you from unfair collectors. The law technically only applies to collection agencies (not your creditor), but later court cases make most creditors also abide by the FFDCPA.

- The Act states that harassment is illegal, and restricts a collector's calls between the hours of ______________ and ______________ (unless they have your permission).

- The Act also allows you to demand that a creditor cease calling you at ______________. You should request this in writing by certified mail with return receipt requested.

- The Act even allows you to insist that a creditor stop ________ contact except to notify you of ____________ proceedings.

- Do not use a cease-and-desist letter except in horrible situations, because all ____________________ stop and any hope of a positive resolution is lost.

- No collector or creditor may _________ a bank account or garnish (attach) ___________ without proper and lengthy court action, except in the case of delinquent IRS or student loan debt. All such threats are a bluff.

"Better not to vow than to vow and not pay."

– Ecclesiastes 5:5 (NKJV)

"A good name is to be chosen rather than great riches, loving favor rather than silver and gold."

– Proverbs 22:1 (NKJV)

Pro Rata Plan

Your plan should include as much prompt repayment of debt as possible, but YOU must set your priorities of repayment. Do NOT let a collector use your credit report as a

______________ ______________.

When you are unable to pay the minimum payments, use the _______ __________ plan.

"I've never been poor, only broke. Being poor is a frame of mind. Being broke is only a temporary position."

– Mike Todd

"A light purse is a heavy curse."

– Benjamin Franklin

Always set your priorities by the Four Walls:

1. Food
2. Shelter
3. Clothing
4. Transportation

NOTES

Pro Rata Debts (Instructions)

"Pro rata" means the fair share, or the percent of your total debt each creditor represents. This will determine how much you should send them when you cannot make the minimum payments. Even if you cannot pay your creditors what they request, you should pay everyone as much as you can. Send the check for their pro rata share, along with a copy of your budget and this form, every month. *Do this even if the creditor says they will not accept it.*

Do you need to use the pro rata plan?

First, use your monthly cash flow plan to determine your total disposable income. Simply write down your income on the line at the top of the form. Then, write down the total you spend on necessities (not including consumer debt) each month. Subtract the necessity expense from the income, and you are left with your disposable income. This is the money you have to put toward your debts.

Second, add up your total amount of debt, not including your home, and write that in the blank provided. Below that, write in the total of the minimum monthly payments on all your debts. If the total of your minimum payments is greater than your total disposable income, you need to use the pro rata plan.

For example, Joe and Suzie have a total debt of $2,000, with a combined total minimum payment of $310. However, this family only has $200 in disposable income each month, which means they do not have enough money to make the minimum payments. So, they will use the pro rata plan to give each creditor their fair share of the family's $200.

How to Use This Form

This form has six columns:

1. **Item:** the name and type of the account.
2. **Total Payoff:** the total amount due on the account.
3. **Total Debt:** the combined total of all your debts.
4. **Percent:** the portion of the total debt load that each account represents. You can calculate this by simply dividing the Total Payoff by the Total Debt for each line.
5. **Disposable Income:** the amount of money you have left after paying necessities.
6. **New Payment:** the amount that you will now send to each creditor. You calculate this by multiplying the numbers in each line's Percent and Disposable Income columns.

The pro rata plan helps you to meet your obligations to the best of your ability. Of course, your creditors will not like receiving less than their required minimum payments. However, if you keep sending them checks, they'll most likely keep cashing them. We have had clients use this plan, even when sending only $2, who have survived for years.

Pro Rata Debt List (Form 11)

Income		$3361
Necessity Expense	–	$3161
Disposable Income	=	$200

Total Debt:	$2,000
Total Minimum Payments:	$310

Item	Total Payoff		Total Debt		Percent		Disposable Income		New Payment
J.C. Penney	100	/	2,000	=	5% (.05)	X	200	=	$10
Sears	200	/	2,000	=	10% (.10)	X	200	=	$20
MBNA Visa	200	/	2,000	=	10% (.10)	X	200	=	$20
Citibank Visa	300	/	2,000	=	15% (.15)	X	200	=	$30
Discover	1200	/	2,000	=	60%(.60)	X	200	=	$120
		/		=		X		=	
		/		=		X		=	
		/		=		X		=	
		/		=		X		=	
		/		=		X		=	
		/		=		X		=	
		/		=		X		=	
		/		=		X		=	
		/		=		X		=	
		/		=		X		=	
		/		=		X		=	
		/		=		X		=	
		/		=		X		=	
		/		=		X		=	

Lawsuits

Eventually, if you are making no payments and have cut no deals, you will get sued.

Typically, lawsuits for under $____________ are filed in General Sessions Court (or small claims court), which is a fairly informal proceeding.

Before you are sued, you will be served by the local sheriff's department and typically given _______ days notice of the court date.

In court, if the debt is valid, even if you fight, you will _______. From that date you will generally have 30 days before the _______________ becomes final and garnishments or attachments begin.

At ANY TIME during the process, you may settle with the creditor or their attorney in writing. If you are not able to reach an agreement, you can file with the court a "________ _________ motion," called a "pauper's oath" in some states.

"And if anyone wants to sue you and take your shirt, let him have your coat also. Whoever forces you to go one mile, go with him two. Give to him who asks of you, and do not turn away from him who wants to borrow from you."

– Matthew 5:40-42 (NASB)

"Do not withhold good from those to whom it is due, when it is in the power of your hand to do so. Do not say to your neighbor, 'Go, and come back, and tomorrow I will give it,' when you have it with you."

– Proverbs 3:27-28 (NKJV)

Facts You Should Know

- Payment history on your credit file is supplied by credit grantors with whom you have credit. This includes both open accounts and accounts that have already been closed.

- Payment in full does not remove your payment history. The length of time information remains on file is:

  Credit and collection accounts – Seven years from the date of last activity.

  Courthouse records – Seven years from the date filed, except bankruptcy Chapters 7 and 11, which remain for 10 years from date filed.

- A divorce decree does not supersede the original contract with the creditor and does not release you from legal responsibility on any accounts. You must contact each creditor individually and seek their legally binding release of your obligation. Only after that release can your credit history be updated accordingly.

- There may appear to be duplicate accounts reported in your credit file. This could be because some credit grantors issue both revolving and installment accounts. Another reason is that when you move, some credit grantors transfer your account to a different location and issue another account number.

- The balance reported is the balance on the date the source reported the information. Credit grantors supply information on a periodic basis, so the balance shown may not be the balance you know it is today. If the balance reported was correct as of the date reported, it is not necessary to reinvestigate the balance on that account.

NOTES

Credit Bureaus

The FACT Act amendments to the Fair Credit Reporting Act require the nationwide credit bureaus to provide consumers, upon request, one free personal credit report in any 12-month period. You may contact the Central Source online at www.annualcreditreport.com or by calling toll free (877) FACT ACT. Free copies are also available if you have been denied credit in the past 60 days and the creditor used their services.

- EXPERIAN
  Phone: (888) 397-3742
  Website: www.experian.com

- EQUIFAX CREDIT BUREAU
  Phone: (800) 685-1111
  Website: www.equifax.com

- TRANSUNION CREDIT BUREAU
  Phone: (877) 322-8228
  Website: www.transunion.com

- FEDERAL TRADE COMMISSION
  Phone: (202) 326-2222
  Address: 600 Pennsylvania Avenue, N.W.
  Washington, D.C. 20580
  Website: www.ftc.gov
  Publishes a brief, semi-annual list (March and September) on card pricing by the largest issuers for $5 per copy. Offers a number of free credit-related publications.

Be Proactive

Decrease unauthorized direct mail marketing (including pre-approved credit card offers) and unwanted telemarketing calls!

- PRE-SCREENING OPT OUT
  Phone: (888) 567-8688
  Website: www.optoutprescreen.com

- NATIONAL DO NOT CALL REGISTRY
  Phone: (888) 382-1222
  Website: www.donotcall.gov

You can write a letter and request to be removed from direct marketing databases for five years. Be sure to include your name, home phone number, address, and your signature. If your address changes, you must make another request.

- FOR DIRECT MAILINGS:
  Address: Mail Preference Service
  Direct Marketing Association
  P.O. Box 282
  Carmel, NY 10512
  Website: www.dmaconsumers.org/cgi/offmailinglist

- FOR TELEMARKETING:
  Address: Telephone Preference Service
  Direct Marketing Association
  P.O. Box 1559
  Carmel, NY 10512
  Website: www.dmaconsumers.org/cgi/offtelephone

NOTES

Request For File Disclosure Form

REQUEST FOR FILE DISCLOSURE

CREDIT BUREAU OF NASHVILLE

604 FOURTH AVE NORTH - P.O. BOX 190589 - NASHVILLE, TN 37219-0589

Reason for File Disclosure Request ____________________________________

Referred by ____________________________ Was credit refused? yes no

I hereby request the Credit Bureau of Nashville to disclose to me the contents of my credit record. I understand that if I have been rejected for credit within the past sixty (60) days as the result of credit information contained in my credit record, there will be NO CHARGE for this disclosure, otherwise there will be an $8 charge for an individual disclosure or $10 for both myself and my spouse.

Name ____ Phone No. __________

Spouse's Name ____

Present Address ____

City ________________________________, State ______________Zip Code _______

Former Address ____

City ________________________________, State ______________Zip Code _______

Date of Birth ____________________________ Social Security No. ________________

Employed By ____

How Long? ____________________ Position ____________________________________

Former Employment ____

Spouse's Date of Birth ______________________ Social Security No. ________________

Spouse's Employment ____

How Long? ____________________ Position ____________________________________

I hereby authorize the Credit Bureau of Nashville to review my credit record with me, to make any necessary investigation of my credit transactions and to furnish to its subscribers reports based thereon. In consideration of its undertaking to make such an investigation I authorize any business or organization to give full information and records about me.

I am the person named above and I understand that federal law provides that a person who obtains information from a consumer reporting agency under false pretenses shall be fined not more than $5,000 or imprisoned no more than one year or both.

Signed ____ Date _______________

Telephone Number _____________ Ext ________ where I can be reached during normal working hours.

AUTHORIZATION FOR DISCLOSURE OF SPOUSE'S CREDIT RECORD

I, __________________, certify that I am presently married to __________________, and am acting in his/her behalf in reviewing the credit record information concerning him/her maintained by the Credit Bureau of Nashville.

Sample Removal Letter

Date ______________________

(From)

____

____

____

VIA: Certified Mail, Return Receipt Requested

(To)
Mail Preference Service
Direct Marketing Association
P.O. Box 282
Carmel, NY 10512

RE: Unauthorized direct marketing and pre-approved credit card offers

This letter is your formal notice to remove my name from all direct marketing and pre-screening databases. I do not wish to receive any unsolicited offers, especially from credit card companies.

Not only do I request that my name be permanently removed, but I also request that my phone number and address must likewise be permanently removed. My correct information is as follows:

(Complete Name)

(Full Address)

(Phone Number with Area Code)

Thank you for your immediate attention to this matter.

Sincerely,

(Signatures)

Sample Cease and Desist Letter

Date ______________________

(From)

____

____

____

VIA: Certified Mail, Return Receipt Requested

(To)

____

____

____

RE: ____________________________

Dear ____________________,

You are hereby notified under provisions of Public Law 95-109, Section 805-C, the FAIR DEBT COLLECTION PRACTICES ACT to CEASE AND DESIST in any and all attempts to collect the above debt.

Your failure to do so WILL result in charges being filed against you with the state and federal regulatory agencies empowered with enforcement.

Please be further warned that if ANY derogatory information is placed on any credit reports after receipt of this notice, that too will result in action being taken against you.

PLEASE GIVE THIS MATTER YOUR IMMEDIATE ATTENTION.

Sincerely,

____

(Signature)

Sample Credit Bureau Letter

Date ______________________

(From)

____

____

____

(To)

____

____

____

RE: ______________________

In reviewing the attached credit bureau report issued by your agency, I have detected an error. The following account(s) is/are reported inaccurately:

Company Name:______________________________
Account Number: ____________________________

Under the provisions of the 1977 Federal Fair Credit Reporting Act, I hereby request that your agency prove to me in writing the accuracy of the reporting of this account. Under the terms of the Act and succeeding court cases, you have 30 days to prove such accuracy or remove the account entirely from my report. I ask that you do so.

This letter was sent certified mail, return receipt requested. I expect a response within the 30-day period. Should I not hear promptly from you, I will follow up with whatever action necessary to cause my report to be corrected.

Please feel free to call me if you have any questions. My home phone number is ________________, and my office number is ________________.

Sincerely,

____

(Signature)

Sample Creditor Letter

Date ______________________

(From)

____
____
____

(To)

____
____
____

RE: ______________________

Dear ______________________,

I am writing to formally request that, in accordance with the 1977 Federal Fair Debt Collection Practices Act, your firm (or any agency hired by your firm) no longer contact me at my place of employment, ______________________.

Please take note that this letter was mailed certified mail, return receipt requested, so that I will have proof that you are in receipt of this letter should legal action against you become necessary.

I am willing to pay the debt I owe you, and I will be in touch soon to work out arrangements.

Feel free to contact me at my home between __________ a.m. and __________ p.m. at the following number: ______________________, or by mail at my home address: ____.

Please give this matter your immediate attention.

Sincerely,

____

(Signature)

Sample Pro Rata Plan Letter

Date: February 22, 2006

From: Joe and Suzie Public
123 Anystreet
Anytown, ST 11111

To: Mega Credit Card Company
999 Main Street
Big City, ST 00000

Re: Joe and Suzie Public # 1234-5678-9012-9999

Dear Collection Manager:

Recently I lost my job. My wife is employed in a clerical position. We have met with a financial counselor to assess our present situation.

We acknowledge our indebtedness to you of $6,000 and fully intend to pay you back in full. However, you are one of six creditors to whom we owe a total of $42,968. We owe minimum payments of $782 each month. We are not able to meet these minimum payments at the present time, and we will not go further into debt to meet these obligations.

We have put together a cash flow plan based on our take-home pay of $2,340 per month (see the enclosed copy of cash flow plan). Since we have two small children and no disposable income, we cannot make a payment to you at the present time, but we do not intend to go bankrupt.

We are asking for a moratorium on payments for the next 120 days. We will keep in close contact with you, and as soon as possible, we will begin making payments. If possible, we further request a reduction in interest during this time.

We are aware that this is an inconvenience to you, but we must meet the basic needs of our family first. We fully intend to pay our creditors all that we owe them. Please be patient with us. If you have any questions please contact us at 600-555-9876.

Thank you for your consideration of our present situation.

Sincerely,

Joe Public
Suzie Public

Answer Key

Credit
Score
Debt
Winning
7
10
Inaccurate
79%
25%
30%
22%
Annually
Fraud
Victim
Police
Report
Theft
Nothing

Nothing
Division
Documentation
Persistent
Hobby
Remove
Certified
Entire
Complaints
Plan
Money
Salespeople
Telemarketers
Turnover
Emotion
Necessities
You
8:00 a.m.

9:00 p.m.
Work
All
Lawsuit
Negotiations
Take
Wages
Paper
Club
Pro
Rata
$10,000
10
Lose
Judgment
Slow
Pay

Set Your Goals for the Week / Gazelle Focus

I will check my credit report for accuracy by this date:

Also this week, I am going to . . .

Review of Last Week

1. What are the six steps to getting out of debt?
2. What are the seven Baby Steps (in order)?
3. Why is it important to complete Baby Step 1 before moving on to Baby Step 2?

Small Group Discussion and Accountability

1. For those of you who have been contacted by a collector or creditor, what emotions have you experienced?
2. In what way is *emotion* a collector's best weapon?
3. Have you ever let a collector set your family's priorities?
4. What are the "Four Walls"? Why is it important to always pay necessities first before paying your creditors, such as credit card companies?
5. True or False: A collector can garnish your wages at any time.
6. Has anyone here been a victim of identify theft? How has that impacted your life?

Homework

1. **Review your credit report.** You can get a free copy from each of the three credit agencies once a year. Check it for accuracy immediately!
2. ***Financial Peace Revisited*:** Read chapters 9 and 22.

online resources

Be sure to check out the special online features for this week.

- **Free Credit Report:** Learn how to get a free copy of your credit report online every year.
- **National Do Not Call List:** Stop those annoying telemarketer calls with the U.S. National Do Not Call Registry.
- **Prescreen Opt-Out:** End all of the "pre-approved" credit offers that fill up your mailbox by automatically turning away any company that tries to check your credit without your knowledge.
- **Identity Theft Protection:** Find out about the only ID theft protection that Dave recommends.

Don't Forget...

It's Week 6 — Time to Update Your Financial Snapshot!

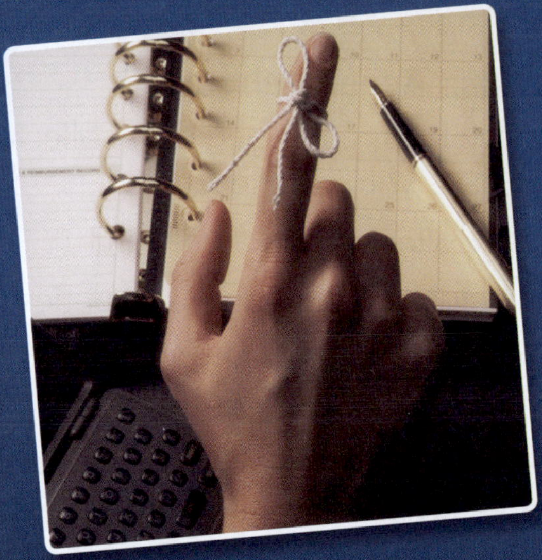

You can do this quickly and easily online as you take advantage of all the great bonus tools and features of the

Member Resource Center

daveramsey.com/fpumember

Dave Ramsey's
Financial Peace® UNIVERSITY

Buyer Beware™

The Power of Marketing on Your Buying Decisions

"He who dies with the most toys is still dead."

– Anonymous

"The blessing of the LORD makes one rich, and He adds no sorrow with it."

– Proverbs 10:22 (NKJV)

"A wise man will hear and increase in learning, and a man of understanding will attain wise counsel."

– Old Proverb

"The plans of the diligent lead to profit, as surely as haste leads to poverty."

– Old Proverb

Caveat Emptor (Let The Buyer Beware)

Profile of the Enemy

(The enemy of your Financial Peace)

Companies use every angle to aggressively compete for your ________________.

Four Major Ways:

1. __________ selling

2. ________________ as a marketing tool

    - _____% of 90 days same-as-cash contracts convert to payments which are usually at ____% APR with Rule of 78's prepayment penalty.

3. ________, ____________, _____________, and other media

4. Product ______________________

✔ Brand Recognition ✔ Shelf Position

✔ Color ✔ Packaging

Significant Purchases

A "significant purchase" is normally anything over $_________. Our bodies go through physiological _________ when making a significant purchase.

We all have that spoiled, red-faced, grocery store kid living inside of us. His name is ___________.

What To Do

Because you can always spend more than you _________, you must develop a power over ___________ by:

1. Waiting __________________ before making a purchase.
2. Carefully considering your buying _____________. No amount of _______ equals contentment or fulfillment.
3. Never buying anything you do not _____________.
4. Considering the "_____________ ______" of your money.
5. Seeking the _____________ of your spouse.

"Who can find a virtuous wife? For her worth is far above rubies. The heart of her husband safely trusts her; so he will have no lack of gain."
– Proverbs 31:10-11 (NKJV)

"Almost any man knows how to make money, but not one in a million knows how to spend it."

– Henry David Thoreau

"For where your treasure is, there your heart will be also."

– Matthew 6:21 (NKJV)

"He who is impulsive exalts folly."

– Proverbs 14:29 (NKJV)

NOTES

Answer Key

Money
Personal
Financing
88
24
TV
Radio
Internet
Positioning
$300
Changes

Immaturity
Make
Purchase
Overnight
Motives
Stuff
Understand
Opportunity
Cost
Counsel

Set Your Goals for the Week / Gazelle Focus

I will sit down with my spouse or accountability partner this week to review the five steps to power over purchase and make myself accountable for following these guidelines.

Also this week, I am going to . . .

Review of Last Week

1. What are collectors trained to do?
2. Who should set the priorities for your family—you or the collectors?
3. How often should you check your credit report? Why?
4. What are the Four Walls?
5. Name the seven Baby Steps in order.

Small Group Discussion and Accountability

1. How do marketers use emotion to compel you to purchase their goods?
2. How can waiting overnight before making a purchase change your behavior? Would you have as much debt now if you had always waited overnight?
3. How would you define a "major purchase"? Why is it so important for married couples to agree on major purchases?
4. What can singles do to guard themselves against impulsive buying decisions?
5. How can you ensure that you will genuinely enjoy your purchases?
6. True or False: I do not borrow money anymore, including using credit cards. Why or why not?
7. In what ways has having an accountability partner been helpful to you? Do you still need help in this area?

Homework

1. **Complete your second Financial Snapshot,** either online or on the paper form included with this workbook.
2. **Memorize the five keys to gaining power over your purchases** and make yourself accountable to someone for following these principles for every major purchase.
3. ***Financial Peace Revisited*:** Read chapter 5.

online resources™

Be sure to check out the special online features for this week.

- **Stupid Tax Forum:** Laugh with others as you share your own stupid tax stories!
- **Do Not Call List:** End the dinnertime telemarketing calls by adding yourself to the national "Do Not Call" list.
- **Buyer Beware Testimonies:** Listen to some great Buyer Beware stories we've collected from other FPU members.

Share Your FPU Story!
"We changed our family tree!"
"FPU saved our marriage!"
"We're debt free!"
"I have an incredible future!"
Tell your "We Did It" story at
daveramsey.com

Dave Ramsey's Financial Peace University

Clause and Effect™

The Role of Insurance in Your Financial Plan

Understanding Insurance

"A prudent man sees evil and hides himself, the naive proceed and pay the penalty."

– Old Proverb

Insurance is an essential financial planning tool.

The purpose of insurance is to ________________ risk.

Without proper insurance, certain losses can ________________ you. Conventional wisdom says that you should transfer that risk.

Basic Types of Coverage Needed

1. Homeowner's or Renter's Insurance
2. Auto Insurance
3. Health Insurance
4. Disability Insurance
5. Long-Term Care Insurance
6. Identity Theft Protection
7. Life Insurance

Do a break-even analysis to see if lowering your deductible makes sense. Compare your annual premium savings with a lower deductible to the extra risk you would take on in the event of an accident.

Types of Insurance

- **Homeowner's and Auto Insurance**

  If you have a full emergency fund, raise your ____________.

  Carry adequate _________________.

  Consider dropping your _______________ on older cars.

  Homeowner's insurance should be "guaranteed __________________ cost."

  _______________ liability policies are a good buy once you have some assets.

- **Health Insurance**

  Keys to saving on your health premiums:

  Increase your ________________ and/or coinsurance amount.

  Increase your______________-__________, but never decrease your maximum pay.

  See if an ____________, a Health Savings Account, would make sense for your situation.

  The HSA is a __________-________________ savings account for medical expenses that works with a high deductible insurance policy.

Medical debt is consistently one of the leading causes for personal bankruptcy. ***You must have health insurance!***

NOTES

Disability insurance is a long-term solution. Your short-term needs should be covered by a full emergency fund of three to six months of expenses.

- **Disability Insurance**

  Disability insurance is designed to replace ____________ lost due to a short-term or permanent disability.

  Try to buy disability insurance that pays if you cannot perform the job that you were educated or ___________ to do.

  That is called ___________________, or "own occ," disability. Many times, this is only available for two years.

  Beware of ___________-term policies covering less than ____ years.

  Your coverage should be for _____% of your current income.

  The _________________ period is the time between the disabling event and when the payments actually begin.

  A ________________ elimination period will _______________ your premium cost.

Even if it's not time to get long-term care insurance for yourself, you may need to have this discussion with your parents.

- **Long-Term Care Insurance**

  Long-term care insurance is for ___________ home, assisted living facilities, or in-home care.

  _____% of people over the age of 65 will require long-term care at some point in their lives.

- **Identity Theft Protection**

  Don't buy ID theft protection that only provides credit report _________________.

  Good protection includes ___________________ services that assign a ________________________ to clean up the mess.

- **Life Insurance**

  Life insurance is to replace lost income due to ___________.

  Most people have no ________________ what kind of life insurance they ________________.

  Two Types of Life Insurance:

  1. _______________ insurance is for a specified period, is substantially cheaper, and has no savings plan built into it.

  2. ____________ ____________ insurance is normally for life and is more expensive because it funds a savings plan.

  The most common insurance myth is that the need for life insurance is a ________________ situation.

  Twenty years from today, when the children are grown and gone, you are debt-free (including that 15-year mortgage), and you have investments that have grown to a substantial amount, you will have become self-__________________.

Human beings have a 100% mortality rate—we're all going to die someday. If people depend on your income, it is your responsibility to make sure they'll be taken care of if something were to happen to you.

"It is unwise to hope for the best without preparing for the worst."

– Anonymous

"For what is your life? It is even a vapor that appears for a little time and then vanishes away."

– James 4:14 (NKJV)

NOTES

Why Not Life Insurance as an Investment?

If you try to play "sophisticated" games with insurance, you will get burned.

Keep your insurance and investments separate. Don't try to do any wealth building in your insurance plan. It just doesn't work.

1. Returns are historically __________.

2. When you die with cash value, the insurance company ____________ the cash value.

3. The _________________ deducted from your return are extremely ________________.

Cash Value vs. Term + Roth IRA

For $145 a month, you could have $125,000 in cash value insurance. Or, for that same $145, you could pay $10 for $400,000 in 20-year term insurance *and* invest $135 into a Roth IRA. If you start at age 30...

Age	$125,000 Cash Value Guaranteed	$135/mo in Roth 12% Return
50	$27,598	$133,000
70	$65,761	$1,500,000

Before You Cancel Your Cash Value Policy...

Make sure that you already have a new term policy in place! If, for some reason, you cannot be approved for a new term policy, it is better to hang on to a bad cash value policy than to have nothing at all—*until you become self-insured.*

What To Remember When Purchasing Life Insurance:

1. Buy only low-cost level ______________.
2. Do not forget your _________________.
3. Stay away from fancy _________________.
4. Children only need enough for _______________ expenses.

You need about ______ times your income. Invested at 10-12%, the annual interest would replace your lost income.

Insurance to Avoid

1. _______________ life and disability
2. Credit _______________ protection
3. _______________ and hospital indemnity
4. Accidental _________________
5. Any insurance with ___________ ____________, investments, or refund
6. Pre-paid ________________ policies
7. _______________ life insurance
8. Any kind of ________________ coverage

A stay-at-home mom brings enormous economic value to a home. If something were to happen to her, dad would need the money to replace part of what mom does.

NOTES

Answer Key

Transfer	Occupational	Idea	Options
Bankrupt	Short	Own	Burial
Deductible	5	Term	10
Liability	65%	Cash	Credit
Collision	Elimination	Value	Card
Replacement	Longer	Permanent	Cancer
Umbrella	Lower	Insured	Death
Deductible	Nursing	Low	Cash
Stop-Loss	69%	Keeps	Value
HSA	Monitoring	Fees	Burial
Tax-Sheltered	Restoration	High	Mortgage
Income	Counselor	Term	Duplicate
Trained	Death	Spouse	

Set Your Goals for the Week / Gazelle Focus

I will have all necessary insurance plans in place by this date:

Also this week, I am going to . . .

Review of Last Week

1. Name five keys to power over purchase. Did you discuss these things with your spouse or accountability partner this week?
2. Complete this statement: "FPU has helped my life by...."

Small Group Discussion and Accountability

1. What do you do if money is tight:
   A. Drop your insurance until you've paid off your debts.
   B. Put insurance only on the person who brings home the most income and pray nothing happens to the rest of the family.
   C. Make insurance a priority to avoid a financial disaster.
2. What could happen to you financially if you do not have the proper amount of insurance in place?
3. How does having an emergency fund affect your insurance premiums and deductibles?
4. What is the difference between term and cash value life insurance?
5. What happens to your cash savings inside of a cash value life insurance plan when you die?
6. Why is it so important to make sure your homeowner's policy includes guaranteed replacement cost?
7. Why do you think so few people carry long-term disability coverage? Why is this so dangerous?

Homework

1. **Complete the Insurance Coverage Recap form** in the back of this book. Make sure your spouse or other beneficiaries know where to locate this form in an emergency.
2. **Identify any insurance policies** that need to be changed or added to your financial plan.
3. **Calculate how much life insurance coverage you need** based on Dave's principles.
4. ***Financial Peace Revisited*:** Read chapter 11 (only the subtitled section "Insurance").

online resources™

Be sure to check out the special online features for this week.

- **Identity Theft Protection:** Learn more about the ID theft policy that Dave recommends.
- **Get Help:** Find a reliable health insurance representative in your area with the heart of a teacher. If you need help, check out Dave's Endorsed Local Provider network.
- **Bonus Video:** Watch as Dave takes a call on the radio show from a listener with insurance questions.
- **Testimonies:** Read how others learned these insurance lessons—the hard way!

Dave Ramsey's

Financial Peace® UNIVERSITY

That's Not Good Enough!™

How To Buy Only Big, Big Bargains

Ground Rules For Big Bargains

You cannot have healthy relationships and build wealth with lies as your foundation.

It is proper to get a great deal if you:

1. Have in no way ____________________ the truth.
2. Have not set out to __________ the other party.
3. Have created a _________ - _________ deal.

The First Key

The first key to opening the door to huge bargains is learning to _______________ everything.

Win-win deals really work, so don't be ___________ to _________ for the deal!

Lucky Seven Basic Rules of Negotiating

1. Always tell the absolute ________________.

2. Use the power of _______________.

    - Cash is ____________________.

    - Cash is ____________________.

    - Cash has _______________.

3. Understand and use "_________ _________ power."

4. ____________ _________.

5. "That's not _____________ ______________."

6. _____________ guy, _________ guy.

7. The "If I" __________ __________ technique.

"Dishonest scales are an abomination to the LORD, but a just weight is His delight."

– Proverbs 11:1 (NKJV)

"Probably the world's greatest humorist was the man who named them 'easy payments.'"

– Stanislas

NOTES

"Remember, what you possess in the world will be found at the day of your death to belong to someone else, but what you are will be yours forever."

– Henry Van Dyke

"A man who owns little is little owned."

– Anonymous

"But the fruit of the Spirit is love, joy, peace, patience, kindness, goodness, faithfulness, gentleness, and self-control. Against these things there is no law."

– Galatians 5:22-23 (NIV)

The Second Key

- The second key to opening the door to huge bargains is that you must have ______________.
- Don't get __________________ to a purchase.

The Third Key

- The third key to opening the door to huge bargains is that you must know ___________ to __________ deals.
- ______________ something of value, goods, or just your ___________________.

Places to Find Great Deals

1. ________________
2. Estate Sales
3. ________ __________
4. Couponing
5. __________ ________
6. Repo Lot
7. ________ ___________
8. Refunding
9. ________________
10. Pawn Shops
11. _________ ____________
12. Classified Ads
13. _______________ _______
14. Conventions

Love, Mom

During a period of economic hardship due to high interest rates in the real estate business, my mother sent me the following poem in the mail.

THE ROOSTER AND THE HEN

Said the Little Red Rooster, "Believe me things are tough!
Seems the worms are getting scarcer and I cannot find enough.
What's become of all those fat ones? It's a mystery to me.
There were thousands through that rainy spell,
But now, where can they be?"

But the Old Black Hen who heard him didn't grumble or complain,
She had lived through lots of dry spells;
She had lived through floods of rain.
She picked a new and undug spot, The ground was hard and firm,
"I must go to the worms," she said. "The worms won't come to me."

The Rooster vainly spent his day,
Through habit, by the ways
Where fat round worms had passed in squads back in the rainy days.
When nightfall found him supperless, he growled in accents rough,
"I'm hungry as a fowl can be, conditions sure are tough."

But the Old Black Hen hopped to her perch
And dropped her eyes to sleep
And murmured in a drowsy tone, "Young man, hear this and weep.
I'm full of worms and happy
For I've eaten like a pig.
The worms were there as always
But, boy I had to dig!"

This was a Depression Era Poem. Strange it still applies today.

Love,

Mom

Answer Key

Misrepresented
Harm
Win-Win
Negotiate
Afraid
Ask
Truth
Cash
Emotional
Visual
Immediacy
Walk
Away

Shut Up
Good
Enough
Good
Bad
Take
Away
Patience
Married
Where
Find
Trade
Services

Individuals
Public
Auctions
Garage
Sales
Flea
Markets
Foreclosures
Online
Auctions
Consignment
Sales

Set Your Goals for the Week / Gazelle Focus

I am going to pay with cash and negotiate a better price the next time I . . .

Also this week, I am going to . . .

Review of Last Week

1. The purpose of insurance is to:

   A. Lower risk B. Transfer risk C. Eliminate risk

2. True or False: Insurance is an essential planning tool. Why or why not?
3. At what point in the Baby Steps should insurance be included in your financial plan?
4. Hold up your monthly zero-based budget.

   A. Discuss how much easier or harder it was to do this time compared to the first one. Be *honest* with each other.

   B. Discuss what you have learned about handling money.

Small Group Discussion and Accountability

1. Why do most people avoid negotiating for deals?
2. Describe a time when you found a great bargain. Was it a win-win?
3. Why is integrity so important in the area of bargain hunting?
4. What are the seven rules of negotiating?
5. How could a business benefit from applying these techniques?
6. How often do you actually ask for a deal when shopping?
7. When you are at the store and the cashier gives you too much money back, what do you do?

   A. Keep it and don't say anything. B. Return it immediately.

8. Are you still plagued by impulse purchases? What goes through your heart and mind when you are tempted to spend?
9. How is your envelope system coming along? Are you sticking to your written budget?

Homework

1. **Tell a friend about FPU.** If *Financial Peace University* is making a difference in your life, share the good news with someone!
2. ***Financial Peace Revisited*:** Read chapter 13.

online resources™

Be sure to check out the special online features for this week.

- **Bargain Bragging:** Hear other FPU students' bargain hunting success stories!
- **Online Deals:** Check out some great places for online deals and peer reviews.

Dave Ramsey's Financial Peace® UNIVERSITY

Of Mice and Mutual Funds™

Understanding Investments

"Risk comes from not knowing what you're doing."

– Warren Buffett

KISS Rule of Investing

- Keep it ____________, ______________!
- It does not mean that you are stupid if you make ____________ investments.
- Never invest purely for __________ ____________________.
- Never invest using _________________ money.

Remember Grandma's advice: Don't put all your eggs in one basket.

Diversification

- Diversification means to _______________ ______________.
- Diversification ______________ risk.

The Power of Diversification

Investor 1
- Invest $10,000 for 25 years at 7%

Investor 2
- Invest $2,000 and lose it all
- Invest $2,000 under your mattress
- Invest $2,000 at 5% return
- Invest $2,000 at 10% return
- Invest $2,000 at 15% return

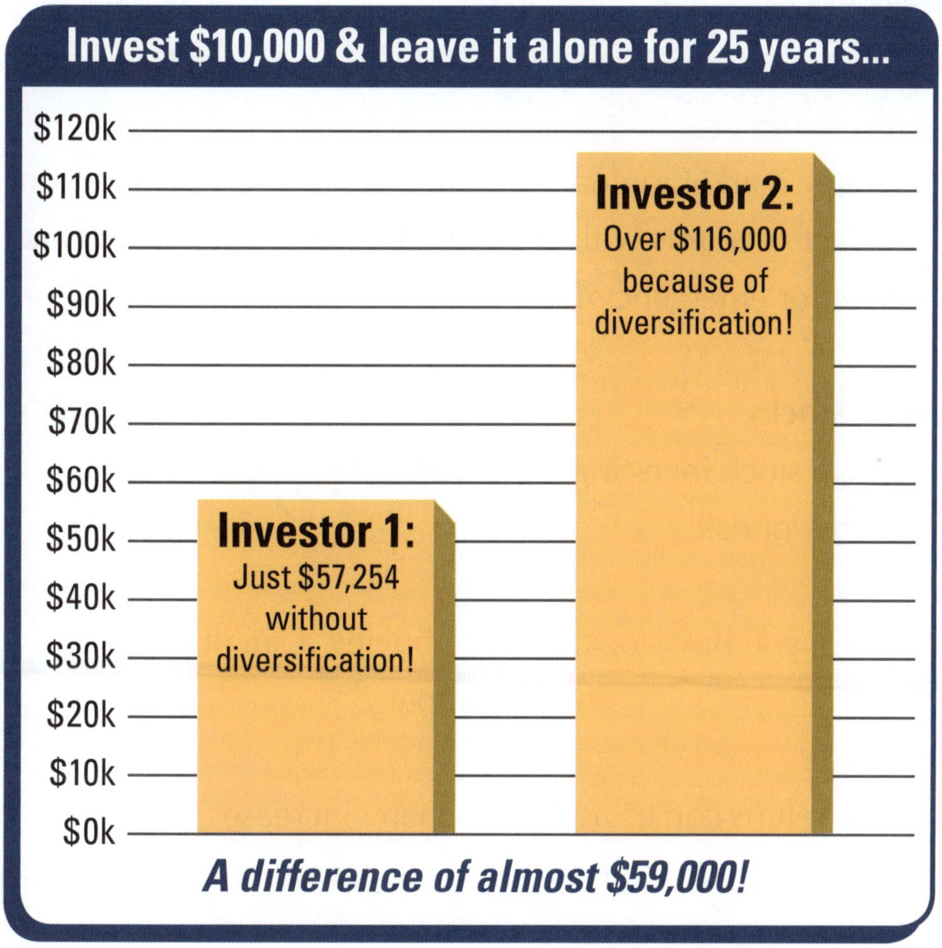

"Give portions to seven, yes to eight, for you do not know what disaster may come upon the land."

– Ecclesiastes 11:2 (NIV)

NOTES

Risk Return Ratio and Liquidity

- With virtually all investments, as the __________ goes up, so does the potential ______________.

- When discussing investments, liquidity is ____________.

- As there is more liquidity, there is typically ______ return.

Types of Investments

1. Money Markets

- A C.D. is a certificate of _________, typically at a bank.

- Money market mutual funds are _________ risk money market accounts with check-writing privileges. These are great for emergency funds.

2. Single Stocks

- Single stock investing carries an extremely __________ degree of risk.

- When you buy stock, you are buying a small piece of ____________ in the company.

- Your return comes as the company increases in __________ or pays you, its owner, some of the profits (called _____________).

"Behold the turtle who only makes progress when he sticks his neck out."

– Anonymous

"October. This is one of the peculiarly dangerous months to speculate in stocks. The others are July, January, September, April, November, May, March, June, December, August, and February."

– Mark Twain

"A faithful man will abound with blessings, but he who hastens to be rich will not go unpunished."

– Old Proverb

3. Bonds

- A bond is a ____________ instrument by which the company owes ______________ money.
- Your return is the fluctuation in price and the __________ rate paid. __________ individuals do well with single bond purchases.

4. Mutual Funds

- Investors pool their ________________ to invest.
- Professional portfolio managers manage the pool or _________________.
- Your ________________ comes as the _______________ of the fund is increased.
- Mutual funds are good ______________ term investments.

Standard Mutual Fund Diversification

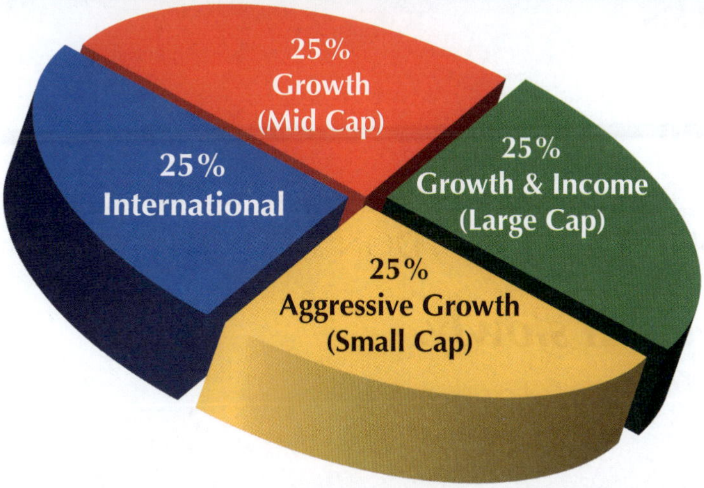

"An investment in knowledge always pays the best interest."

– Ben Franklin

"I'm putting all my money in taxes. It's the only thing guaranteed to go up."

– Mark Twain

Conservative Diversification:

25% – Balanced
25% – Growth
25% – Growth & Income
25% – International

NOTES

Variable annuities are good for older people because the principal can be guaranteed.

You can name a beneficiary so the money passes outside of probate, and you can use them when you have maxed out all your other sheltered retirement options.

NEVER use annuities inside retirement options; instead, go straight to mutual funds. There is no sense paying the annuity fee to get a tax deferment that you already have in your retirement plan.

5. Rental Real Estate

- Least ______________ consumer investment.
- You should have a lot of __________________ before using real estate as an investment.

6. Annuities

- Annuities are _______________ accounts with an insurance company.
- ________ annuities are at a low interest rate of around 5%, aren't *really* fixed, and are a bad long-term investment.
- ______________ annuities are mutual funds sheltered by the annuity covering, thereby allowing the mutual fund to grow tax-deferred.

7. Horrible Investments

- Gold
- Commodities & Futures
- Day Trading
- Viaticals

Conclusion

If you do not understand an investment well enough to teach someone else how it works, DON'T BUY IT!

Build wealth slowly.

Monthly Debt Payments Rob You Of Your Retirement!

Years Invested Monthly At 12% Per Year

Monthly Payments	5 years	10 years	15 years	25 years	40 years
$100	8,167	23,004	49,958	187,885	1,176,477
$200	16,334	46,008	99,916	375,769	2,352,954
$300	24,500	69,012	149,874	563,654	3,529,431
$400	32,668	92,015	199,832	751,538	4,705,909
$500	40,835	115,019	249,790	939,423	5,882,386
$600	49,002	138,023	299,748	1,127,308	7,058,863
$700	57,168	161,027	349,706	1,315,193	8,235,341
$800	65,336	184,031	399,664	1,503,077	9,411,818
$900	73,503	207,034	449,622	1,690,962	10,588,295
$1,000	81,669	230,039	499,580	1,878,847	11,764,772
$1,200	98,004	276,046	599,496	2,254,616	14,117,727
$1,500	122,504	345,058	749,370	2,818,270	17,647,159
$2,000	163,339	460,077	999,160	3,757,693	23,529,545

However, retirement can look pretty sweet if you don't have any debt.

NOTES

Answer Key

Simple
Stupid
Simple
Tax
Savings
Borrowed
Spread
Around
Lowers
Risk
Return
Availability

Less
Deposit
Low
High
Ownership
Value
Dividends
Debt
You
Interest
Few
Money

Fund
Return
Value
Long
Liquid
Cash
Savings
Fixed
Variable

Set Your Goals for the Week / Gazelle Focus

I will be ready for Baby Step 4's investing (all debts paid and a fully funded emergency fund) by this date:

Also this week, I am going to . . .

Review of Last Week

1. What are the seven basic rules of negotiating?
2. Did the previous lesson change any of your shopping habits this week?

Small Group Discussion and Accountability

1. Why is investing intimidating to many people? Discuss some experiences with investing.
2. Explain what a mutual fund is and how it works.
3. Why is it dangerous to invest with borrowed money?
4. Why is diversification important?
5. Why are single stocks so dangerous?
6. Why does Dave stress the importance of becoming debt free (except the mortgage) before you begin your long-term investing?
7. Why is it so important to make your own educated, well-informed decisions, rather than simply surrendering your decisions to an advisor?
8. Talk about how important it is for spouses to be on the same page when it comes to dumping debt and investing.

Homework

1. **Calculate how much your debt payments are robbing from your retirement.** Use the chart on page 129.
2. **Complete your third Financial Snapshot,** either online or on the paper form included with this workbook.
3. ***Financial Peace Revisited*:** Read chapter 11 (only through the subtitled section "Simple Discipline Is the Key") and chapter 12 (only through the subtitled section "To Load or Not To Load").

online resources™

Be sure to check out the special online features for this week.

- **Millionaire Calculator:** Discover what a one-time investment now could mean for your retirement!
- **Dave's Investment Strategy:** See exactly what Dave does—and does not do—with his own investment money.
- **Investment Calculator:** Learn the impact of inflation on your savings and investing with our online calculators and money tools!

Dave Ramsey's Financial Peace University

From Fruition To Tuition™

Planning for Retirement and College

This lesson is intended only for information! Because tax laws frequently change and various details have been omitted for the sake of time, you MUST check with your tax advisor to verify this information for your situation BEFORE you act.

Retirement & College Funding

"Dishonest money dwindles away, but he who gathers money little by little makes it grow."

– Old Proverb

"A good man leaves an inheritance for his children's children."

– Proverbs 13:22 (NIV)

Once the emergency fund is in place, you should begin retirement and college funding, which falls within long-term investing for ________________.

Baby Step 4™

Invest ____% of your household income into Roth IRAs and pre-tax retirement plans.

ALWAYS save long-term with tax -________________ dollars.

Tax-favored means that the investment is in a ______________ ___________ or has special tax treatment.

Qualified Plans

- Individual Retirement Arrangement (IRA)
- Simplified Employee Pension Plan (SEPP)
- 401(k), 403(b), 457

"Most people have the will to win, few have the will to prepare to win."

– Bobby Knight

Individual Retirement Arrangement (IRA)

- Everyone with ___________ income is eligible.

- The maximum annual contribution for income earners and non-income producing spouses is $___________ as of 2008.

- Remember: IRA is not a type of _______________ at a bank. It is the *tax treatment* on virtually any type of investment.

Roth IRA

The Roth IRA is an ____________-tax IRA that grows tax -_______________!

If you __________ like we teach, you should use the Roth IRA.

Who is eligible?

- Singles – 100% contribution with income less than $95,000. Phase out between $95,000-$110,000. Not eligible above $110,000.

- Married filing jointly – 100% contribution with income less than $150,000. Phase out between $150,000-$160,000. Not eligible over $160,000.

Why the Roth IRA?

1. More ________________.
2. Higher ______________ at retirement.
3. More ________________.
4. More ________________.

Get the most up-to-date statistics and figures in this lesson's special online resources.

The Roth IRA is named for Senator William Roth (R-Delaware), who authored this section of the Taxpayer Relief Act of 1997.

NOTES

Flexibility:

- Tax-free and penalty-free withdrawals at any time equal to contributions. After the emergency fund is depleted, you have a fall back.

- After five years, you can make tax-free, penalty-free withdrawals of 100% under these conditions:

    1. Over 59 and a half years old
    2. Because of death or disability
    3. First-time home purchase (max $10,000)

Simplified Employee Pension Plan (SEPP)

A ________-employed person may deduct up to _______% of their net profit on the business by investing in a SEPP.

- The maximum deductible amount is $45,000 (as of 2007) and all employees who have been with the firm more than three of the last five years must receive the same percentage of their pay.

401(k), 403(b) & 457 Retirement Plans

Most companies have completely done away with traditional ________________ plans in the last 10-20 years. Some new plans offer a variety of pre-tax choices.

Some companies are now offering the __________ 401(k), which grows tax-free.

"In the business world, the rearview mirror is always clearer than the windshield."

– Warren Buffett

"If I have ever made any valuable discoveries, it has been due more to patient attention than to any other talent."

– Isaac Newton

The Roth 401(k) plan went into effect in 2006, giving employees a tax-free growth 401(k) option.

Do not use a Guaranteed Investment ______________ (GIC) or bond funds to fund your plan.

You should be funding your plan whether your company ____________ or not, but the plans that have company matching provide even greater returns.

Rollovers

You should __________ roll all retirement plans to an IRA when you _____________ the company.

Do not bring the money home!
Make it a ____________ ______________.

You should roll to a Roth IRA ONLY if:

1. You will have saved over $______________ by age 65.

2. You pay your taxes _______ of ______________ and not from the IRA funds.

3. You understand that all taxes will become due on the rollover amount.

Currently, you can only roll an IRA to a Roth IRA if you make LESS than $100,000. This restriction may expire in 2010, in which case you could roll to a Roth regardless of your income.

NOTES

Retirement Loans

Never ____________ against your retirement plan.

Federal Thrift Plan

If you are a federal government worker and have the standard thrift plan, we recommend _________% in the C Fund, ________% in the S Fund, and ____________% in the I Fund.

Our Suggestion

How to fund your 15%:

1. Fund 401(k) or other employer plans up to the ___________ (if applicable).

2. Above the matched amount, fund __________ IRAs. If there is no match, start with Roth IRAs.

3. Complete 15% of your income by going back to your ______ or other company plans.

Note: This is the best plan if you end up with $700,000 or more by age 65, because mandatory retirement withdrawals will cause a higher tax bracket at retirement.

Borrowing against your retirement plan is a bad move. Even though you pay yourself back some interest, it is nowhere close to what you would have earned if you had left the money in the investment. Plus, if you leave the company or die before it is repaid, you or your heirs will have 60 days to pay it back in full or you will be hit with enormous penalties and interest. Don't do it!

online

Need some advice as you start investing?

Find someone in your area who has the heart of a teacher. Never let an advisor make your financial decisions for you. Their job is to teach you how to make *your own* decisions.

If you cannot find someone like this in your area, check out our network of Endorsed Local Providers in this lesson's online resources.

Imagine if...

A 30-year-old couple partially funds a Roth IRA ($500 per month) at 12%. At 70 years old they will have...

$5,882,386.26 — TAX FREE!

Imagine if...

That same 30-year-old couple made $40,000 and saved 15% in a 401(k) ($500 per month) at 12%. At 70 years old they will have...

$5,882,386.26 in the 401(k).

By Retirement

That 30-year-old couple, DEBT FREE, saves $1,000 per month at 12%. At 70 years old, they will have:

Roth IRA	**$5,882,386.26**
401k	**$5,882,386.26**
Total	**$11,764,772.50**

This could be you if you get serious about savings and investments!

online

How quickly could you become a millionaire?

Find out with our investment and millionaire calculators online!

NOTES

A recent report showed that the average graduate of a four-year college has student loan debt of $19,237.

Graduate students pile on even more student loan debt, ranging between $27,000 -114,000.

Check online for the most up-to-date information regarding ESA saving limits.

Do you meet the income requirements for an ESA or an UTMA?

Check this lesson's online resources for up-to-date eligibility requirements.

Baby Step 5™

Save for your children's __________ using tax-favored plans.

First...

Save in an Education Savings Account (ESA), or "Education ________."

- You may save $2,000 (after tax) per year, per child, that grows tax free! So, if you start when your child is born and save $2,000 a year for 18 years, you would only invest a total of $36,000. However, at 12% growth, your child would have $126,000 for college—TAX FREE!

Above that...

If you want to save more or if you don't meet the income limits for an ESA, use a certain type of ______ plan.

- The only type we recommend is one that leaves ______ in control of the mutual fund at all times.

- Never buy a plan that:
  1. __________ your options.
  2. Automatically changes your investments based on the _______ of the child.

Only then...

Move to an ________ or _________ plan.

- While this is one way to save with reduced taxes, it is _____ as good as the other options.
- UTMA/UGMA stands for Uniform ____________ / Gift to Minors Act.
- The account is ________________ in the child's name and a _____________ is named, usually the parent or grandparent. This person is the manager until the child reaches age 21. At age 21 (age 18 for UGMA), they can do with it what they please.

Three "Nevers" of College Saving

1. Never save for college using ____________.
2. Never save for college using ____________ bonds. (Only earns 5-6%)
3. Never save for college using ______________ college tuition. (Only earns 7% inflation rate)

"Train a child in the way he should go, and when he is old he will not turn from it."

– Proverbs 22:6 (NIV)

"The rod and rebuke give wisdom, but a child left to himself brings shame to his mother."

– Proverbs 29:15 (NKJV)

NOTES

Monthly Retirement Planning (Form 12)

Too many people use the READY-FIRE-AIM approach to retirement planning. That's a bad plan. You need to aim first. Your assignment is to determine how much per month you should be saving at 12% interest in order to retire at 65 with the amount you need.

If you save at 12% and inflation is at 4%, then you are moving ahead of inflation at a net of 8% per year. If you invest your nest egg at retirement at 12% and want to break even with 4% inflation, you will be living on 8% income.

Step 1: Annual income (today) you wish to retire on: 50,000

Divide by .08

(Nest egg needed)equals: 625,000

Step 2: To achieve that nest egg you will save at 12%, netting 8% after inflation. So, we will target that nest egg using 8%.

Nest Egg Needed $ 625,000

Multiply by Factor X .000436

Monthly Savings Needed = $272.50

Note: Be sure to try one or two examples if you wait 5 or 10 years to start.

8% Factors (select the one that matches your age)

Your Age	Years to Save	Factor
25	40	.000286
30	35	.000436
35	30	.000671
40	25	.001051
45	20	.001698
50	15	.002890
55	10	.005466
60	5	.013610

Monthly College Planning (Form 13)

In order to have enough for college, you must aim at something. Your assignment is to determine how much per month you should be saving at 12% interest in order to have enough for college.

If you save at 12% and inflation is at 4%, then you are moving ahead of inflation at a net of 8% per year.

Step 1: In today's dollars, the annual cost of the college of your choice is:

Amount per year $ 20,000

X 4 years = $ 80,000

(hint: $15,000 to $25,000 annually)

Step 2: To achieve that college nest egg, you will save at 12%, netting 8% after inflation. So, we will target that nest egg using 8%.

Nest Egg Needed $ 80,000

Multiply by Factor X .003287

Monthly Savings Needed = $262.96

Note: Be sure to try one or two examples if you wait 5 or 10 years to start.

8% Factors
(select the one that matches your child's age)

Child's Age	Years to Save	Factor
0	18	.002083
2	16	.002583
4	14	.003287
6	12	.004158
8	10	.005466
10	8	.007470
12	6	.010867
14	4	.017746

Answer Key

Wealth	Invested	Out	Freezes
15%	Flexibility	Pocket	Age
Favored	Self	Borrow	UTMA
Qualified	15%	60%	UGMA
Plan	Pension	20%	Not
Earned	Roth	20%	Transfer
$5,000	Contract	Match	Listed
Investment	Matches	Roth	Custodian
After	Always	401(k)	Insurance
Free	Leave	College	Savings
Save	Direct	IRA	Pre-paid
Choices	Transfer	529	
Bracket	$700,000	You	

Set Your Goals for the Week / Gazelle Focus

I will take care of my family by having a legal will in place by this date:

Also this week, I am going to . . .

Review of Last Week

1. What does diversification mean and how does it affect your risk in investing?
2. Are mutual funds for long-term or short-term investing?
3. Explain Dave's four-fold diversification strategy for long-term investing.

Small Group Discussion and Accountability

1. What do you think when you see retirement-aged people working in grocery stores? Is that what you want to do when you retire?
2. What motivates you to get serious about your retirement plan?
3. Should you ever *temporarily* stop adding to your retirement plan? If so, why? When should you start up again?
4. Why is it such a bad idea to cash in a retirement plan early in order to get out of debt? What are the dangers of borrowing against a retirement account? Have you ever done this?
5. Does college funding come before or after retirement savings according to the Baby Steps? Why?
6. Would you feel guilty taking care of your own retirement plan before putting money aside for your child's college education?
7. How does living by a monthly budget help you prepare for retirement?

Homework

1. **Complete the Monthly Retirement Planning form** in the forms section of this workbook to determine how much money you should be saving every month for retirement.
2. **Complete the Monthly College Planning form** in the forms section of this workbook if you have children who will be heading to college.
3. ***Financial Peace Revisited*:** Read chapter 12 (beginning with subsection "Funding Those Golden Rocking Chairs").

online resources™

Be sure to check out the special online features for this week.

- **Investment Calculator:** Find out how much you need to save to retire with dignity and independence.
- **Get Investment Help:** Find an investment professional in your area with the heart of a teacher. If you need help, check out our network of Endorsed Local Providers.
- **Extra Forms:** Download printable worksheets to calculate the monthly savings needed for your retirement and college planning goals.

Dave Ramsey's Financial Peace University

Working In Your Strengths™

Careers and Extra Jobs

Change Happens

The average job is now only ______ years in length.

This means that the average worker could have as many as _____ different jobs in his or her working lifetime.

Small business is changing the way we think about work. ______% of the companies in America have fewer than 100 employees.

Discover Your Strengths and Weaknesses

How can you know __________ you ought to be and ________ you ought to be doing if you don't know _______ you are?

Speaker and author Marcus Buckingham has identified some common myths that often rob people of having fulfillment and enjoyment in their careers.

Myth: As you grow, you _____________.

Truth: You do not ____________ your personality.

Myth: You will learn and grow the most in the areas in which you are ______________.

Truth: You grow in your _____________. You will grow the most in the areas that you already know and love the most.

"Commit your works to the LORD, and your thoughts will be established."

– Proverbs 16:3 (NKJV)

"But you, be strong and do not let your hands be weak, for your work shall be rewarded!"

– 2 Chronicles 15:7 (NKJV)

"To find out what one is fitted to do, and to secure an opportunity to do it, is the key to happiness."

– John Dewey

Identify Your Motivation and Passion

Career coach Dan Miller reminds us that __________ is ultimately never enough compensation for doing a job.

Find something that blends your skills, ____________, personality traits, __________, dreams, and _______________.

Understand Your Unique Personality

The _______ profile is a simple test that will yield tremendous insight into how you process decisions and what your natural tendencies may be.

- The D (________________) person is a hard-charging driver that is task-oriented and first looks to ______________.
- The I (________________) person is people-oriented, fun, outgoing, and generally concerned about people-pleasing, so they first look to ______________.
- The S (___________) person is amiable, loyal, does not like conflict, and is concerned about __________.
- The C (_______________) person is analytical, loves detail, factual, can seem rigid, and loves _________________.

"Life is never made unbearable by circumstances but only by lack of meaning and purpose."

– Viktor Frankl

"Know thyself, and to thine own self be true."

– Shakespeare

"The unexamined life is not worth living."

– Socrates

"Until you make peace with who you are, you will never be content with what you have."

– Doris Mortman

NOTES

"Career is a means to an end, not the end."

– Anonymous

"The master in the art of living makes little distinction between his work and his play, his labor and his leisure, his mind and his body, his information and his recreation, his love and his religion.

He hardly knows which is which. He simply pursues his vision of excellence at whatever he does, leaving others to decide whether he is working or playing. To him, he is always doing both."

– James Michener

DISC Personality Profile

Fast ↕ Slow

People ↔ Task

I

Influencing

Otter

25% of people are EXPRESSIVE

Good talkers	Can waste time
Outgoing	Won't be quiet
Entertains others	Loses sight of the task
Impulsive	

D

Dominant

Lion

10% of people are DRIVERS

Takes charge	Can hurt feelings
Likes power	Can turn people off
Bold	Overlooks details
Bottom line	

S

Stable

Golden Retriever

40% of people are AMIABLE

Steady	Slow to act
Loyal	Low profile
Calm	Can seem unenthusiastic
Understanding	

C

Compliant

Beaver

25% of people are ANALYTICAL

Loves detail	Resisitant to change
Very logical	Too serious
Factual	
Can seem rigid	

Job Hunting

Companies do not start out looking for ________. They have a specific __________ and they need someone to meet it.

Develop a strategy:

- Identify your ______________.
- _______________ everything you can about them.

Résumés

When it is time to contact the company, think of it like starting a new ______________________ with a person.

After you target the companies where you would most like to work, you are going to contact them at least three times.

- Introduction _______________
- Cover Letter and Résumé
- ______________ Follow-up

Interviews and jobs come from persistent follow-up and __________________.

"The major difference between successful and unsuccessful job hunters is not skill, education, or ability, but the way they go about their job hunt."

– Anonymous

"The secret of success is focus of purpose."

– Thomas Edison

"Genius is the ability to clearly visualize the objective."

– Anonymous

NOTES

Home-Based Business Ideas:

Accounting
Auditing
Bookkeeping
Columnist
Computer Technician
Copywriter
Customer Service
Data Entry Clerk
Editor
Fundraiser
Graphic Artist
Information Specialist
LAN Manager
Lawyer
Market Researcher
Online Auctions
Probation Officer
Programmer
Public Relations
Real Estate Agent
Records Manager
Reporter
Researcher
Sales Representative
Systems Analyst
Technical Writer
Telemarketer
Transcriber
Translator
Travel Agent
Web Design

Part-Time Job Ideas:

Car Detailing
Carpentry
Handyman
Maid Service
Newspaper Delivery
Pizza Delivery
Waiter
Yard Work

Interviews

Present yourself well. You are the ______________, so make it the best one available.

Be on ________, address everyone by _________, offer a firm, confident __________________, and maintain ______ contact at all times.

Designate a time to _____________ _____ after the interview... and DO IT!

Overtime and Extra Jobs

Raising your income _________-term is a career track issue. Raising it _________-term means the dreaded part-time job.

How do you get started with an extra job?

- Be willing to ________________ to win.
- Have a detailed __________ so you can see the finish line. This gives you hope!
- Choose the _____ or start a ________ - _________ business.
- Don't _________ ______!

Beware! Do not allow your work to be the source of all your satisfaction and self-_______________.

An American Creed

I Do Not Choose to Be a Common Man

It is my right to be uncommon—if I can.

I seek opportunity—not security. I do not wish to be a kept citizen, humbled and dulled by having the state look after me.

I want to take the calculated risk; to dream and to build, to fail and to succeed.

I refuse to barter incentive for a dole. I prefer the challenges of life to the guaranteed existence; the thrill of fulfillment to the stale calm of utopia.

I will not trade freedom for beneficence nor my dignity for a handout. I will never cower before any master nor bend to any threat.

It is my heritage to stand erect, proud and unafraid; to think and act for myself, enjoy the benefit of my creations and to face the world boldly and say, "This I have done."

By Dean Alfange

---

*Originally published in *This Week* Magazine.
Later reprinted in *The Reader's Digest*, October 1952 and January 1954.

The Honorable Dean Alfange was an American statesman born December 2, 1899, in Constantinople (now Istanbul). He was raised in upstate New York. He served in the U.S. Army during World War I and attended Hamilton College, graduating in the class of 1922. He attended Columbia University where he received his law degree and opened a practice in Manhattan. In 1942, Alfange was the American Labor Party candidate for governor of New York and a founder of the Liberal Party of New York. Dean Alfange was also Professor Emeritus at UMass Amherst and a leading figure in various pro-Zionist organizations. Between other actions, in November 1943, he appeared before the House of Representatives and addressed them on the rescue of the Jewish people of Europe. He died in Manhattan at the age of 91 on October 27, 1989.

"Think beyond your lifetime if you want to accomplish something truly worthwhile."

– Walt Disney

"Do not overwork to be rich; because of your own understanding, cease! Will you set your eyes on that which is not? For riches certainly make themselves wings; they fly away like an eagle toward heaven."

– Proverbs 23:4-5 (NKJV)

NOTES

Answer Key

2.1
20
98.3%
Where
What
Who
Change
Outgrow
Weakest
Strengths
Money
Abilities
Values
Passions
DISC
Dominant
Problems
Influencing
People
Stable
Pace
Compliant
Procedure
You
Need
Target
Learn
Relationship
Letter
Phone
Networking
Product
Time
Name
Handshake
Eye
Follow
Up
Long
Short
Sacrifice
Plan
Job
Home
Based
Give
Up
Worth

Set Your Goals for the Week / Gazelle Focus

I will take time to write out my greatest strengths, weaknesses, and passions and compare it to the demands of my current job to see if I'm working in my strengths by this date:

Also this week, I am going to . . .

Review of Last Lesson

1. What is an IRA?
2. Should you ever cash in or borrow against pre-taxed retirement savings early to pay off debt? Why or why not?

Small Group Discussion and Accountability

1. If you could do anything you wanted and money was no object, what would you do? How is your current work preparing you to do that?
2. What areas of growth or education will help you along your career path?
3. Based on your unique personality, what strengths do you bring to the workplace?
4. Answer to yourself—True or False: I am supportive of my spouse's work and encourage him/her for all the hard work he/she does to help provide for the family.
5. Talk about the danger of being a workaholic. How can it affect your life, spirit, and family? Is this a non-issue if you are single?
6. Have you tried any creative home-based business ideas?
7. Discuss some benefits of temporarily working a second job to pay off debts with gazelle intensity.
8. Have you stopped using credit cards for purchases?
9. How has this class helped you so far? Share a victory.

Homework

1. **Review the DISC chart in your workbook** to determine if your current line of work naturally fits within your unique personality style.
2. **Lay out a three-year professional plan** in which you envision exactly what you want to be doing three years from now, whether within your current organization or elsewhere. Then, identify the steps to get there. ***Be prepared to share your plan in the next class session!***
3. ***Financial Peace Revisited*:** Read chapter 6.

online resources™

Be sure to check out the special online features for this lesson.

- **Radio Excerpt:** Listen in as Dave talks to a radio listener about whether or not he should leave his job for another opportunity.
- **Free Podcast:** Don't forget to download one free hour of *The Dave Ramsey Show* every day!

Dave Ramsey's Financial Peace University

Real Estate and Mortgages™

Keeping the American Dream from Becoming a Nightmare

Baby Step 6™

Pay off your home ________.

Selling a Home

When selling a home, you should think like a ____________.

The home should be in "near perfect" condition.

The return on investment of fix-up dollars is ____________.

The most important aspect of preparation is attention to the ___________ appeal.

When selling your home, make sure that it is listed on the ________________.

When selling, statistical research has found that the best realtors are worth _______ than they cost.

The exposure through the __________ Listing Service is worth it.

When selecting a realtor, do not rely on ___________________ or __________________.

Paint, lawn care, wallpaper, etc. make a home sell faster and for more money. So DO IT!

"You never get a second chance to make a good first impression."

– Zig Ziglar

"A man builds a fine house; and now he has a master, and a task for life; he is to furnish, watch, show it, and keep it in repair the rest of his days."

– Ralph Waldo Emerson

These are professionals. you should always
______________ them.

Offering a home ______________ will typically not make a sale. If the buyer asks for a warranty, then consider it with that offer.

Buying a Home

Home ownership is a great investment for three main reasons:

1. It's a ________________ savings plan.

2. It's an ________________ hedge.

3. It grows virtually _______ - ________.

   You can have a gain of $250,000 single or $500,000 married and pay zero tax on the sale of your personal residence if you hold it at least two years.

Title insurance insures you against an ___________ title, which is when your proper ownership is in question. It is a good buy.

Always get a land _______________ if buying more than a standard subdivision lot.

Realtors' access to the ________ system can make house hunting easier, but be careful. Many agents can only think like retailers, which is not what you want when buying.

"Prepare your outside work, make it fit for yourself in the field; and afterward build your house."

– Proverbs 24:27 (NKJV)

NOTES

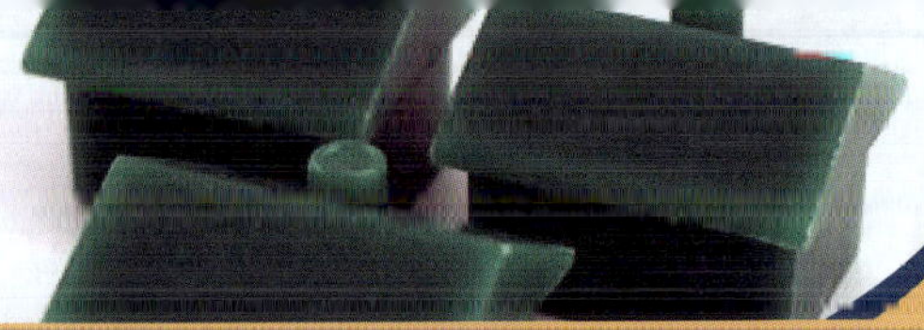

What To Buy

"Any structural weirdness you are willing to overlook will cost you at resale."

– Anonymous

Buy in the ______________ price range of the neighborhood.

Homes appreciate in good neighborhoods and are priced based on three things: __________, ____________, and ___________!

If possible, buy near ___________ or with a _____________.

Buy bargains by ______________ bad landscaping, outdated carpet, ugly wallpaper, and the Elvis print in the master bedroom.

However...

Always buy a home that is (or can be) attractive from the ____________ and has a good basic ________________.

Have the home inspected mechanically and structurally by a certified ____________ ______________.

Appraisals are an "__________ of value," but it's a better opinion than the current homeowner has. Always order one if in doubt.

What Not To Buy

1. ________________ or ______________ ___________

2. ________________

Mortgages

First, remember to ___________ debt.

The best mortgage is the _______% down plan.

But if you must take a mortgage...

Do not buy until you are ready. That means you are out of debt with a fully-funded emergency fund.

There is nothing wrong with _______________ for a little while. This demonstrates ______________ and wisdom.

Get a payment of no more than _____% of your take home pay on a ______________ fixed rate loan, with at least _____% down. Have a fully-funded emergency fund left over after closing.

Why choose a 15-year mortgage?

(Figures based on 6% APR)

I. $225,000	15 years	Pay	$1,899 /mo
II. $225,000	30 years	Pay	$1,349 /mo
		Difference	$550 /mo

But after 10 years...

The 15-year loan has a balance of $98,210 while the 30-year loan has a balance of $188,292!

During that 10 years, you would have paid almost $162,000 on the 30-year mortgage, but only paid down the loan by $36,708!

"For which of you, intending to build a tower, does not sit down first and count the cost, whether he has enough to finish it — lest, after he has laid the foundation, and is not able to finish, all who see it begin to mock him, saying, 'This man began to build and was not able to finish'?"

– Luke 14:28-30 (NKJV)

NOTES

Horrible Mortgage Options

To calculate how an ARM adjusts, see "How to Figure the Change in Your ARM" at the end of this lesson.

1. Adjustable Rate Mortgages (ARMs) were brought on with the advent of ______________ interest rates in the early 1980's.

    - The concept of the ARM is to _____________ the risk of higher interest rates to the _________________ and, in return, the lender gives a lower rate up front.

    - Of course, ______________ _________ loans are a bad idea because you are only paying the interest—*duh!*

    - You can qualify for more home with ARMs, but the risk of financial stress later is not worth it.

The FTC says that reverse mortgage options have the most fraud in the mortgage business.

2. _________________ Mortgages

    - Bad idea because you are putting a paid-for home at risk and the fees are horrible.

3. ___________________, or Bi-Weekly Payoff

    - Allows you to make a half-payment every two weeks, which equals 13 payments a year. The reason it pays off early is because you make one extra payment a year.

    - Do not pay a fee for this option. You can easily do this on your own.

4. __________ Advantages of a Mortgage

- Do not fall for the myth that you should keep your mortgage for the tax advantages. The math doesn't work.

Where's the Tax Advantage?

Mortgage Amount	Interest Rate	Annual Interest Paid
$200,000	**5%**	**$10,000**

Mortgage interest is tax-deductible, so you would not have to pay taxes on this $10,000. That is why many people tell you to keep the mortgage. But what does this really save you?

Taxable Amount	Tax Bracket	Annual Taxes Paid
$10,000	**25%**	**$2,500**

So, if you keep your mortgage just for the "tax advantages," all you are really doing is sending $10,000 to the bank instead of sending $2,500 to the IRS. Where's the ***"advantage"*** in that?

You can avoid PMI with a 20% down payment or by paying your existing mortgage down to 20% loan-to-value.

Basic Ways to Finance a Home

1. ________________, usually through FNMA and privately insured against default.

- Down payments range from 5% to 20% or more.
- These loans are available in all forms and formats.
- PMI is ________________ mortgage insurance.

NOTES

2. ______, which is insured by HUD—the federal government.

- Down payments are as low as ______% and are used on lower-priced homes.
- These loans are currently ____________ expensive than conventional financing and should be avoided.

3. _______, which is insured by the Veterans Administration.

- Designed to benefit the veteran; the seller pays everything, allowing a true zero-down purchase.
- With a good down payment, the conventional loan is a __________ deal.

4. ____________ financing is when you pay the owner over time, making him/her the mortgage holder.

- This is a ___________ way to finance because you can be creative in the structure of the loan.

  Example: No payments for a year, interest rates that graduate, or discount for early payoff.

How To Figure Your New Payment

Monthly Payment per $1,000 in Loan Amount

Rate	15-Year	30-Year
4.5%	7.65	5.07
5.0%	7.91	5.37
5.5%	8.17	5.68
6.0%	8.44	6.00
6.5%	8.71	6.32
7.0%	8.99	6.66
7.5%	9.28	7.00
8.0%	9.56	7.34
8.5%	9.85	7.69
9.0%	10.15	8.05
9.5%	10.44	8.41
10.0%	10.75	8.78
10.5%	11.05	9.15
11.0%	11.37	9.52
11.5%	11.68	9.90
12.0%	12.00	10.29

_________ / 1,000 = _________ X _________ = _____________

Sales Price / 1,000 = #1000's X Factor = Monthly Payment

Example: Sales Price - $150,000, 15 years at 6%

$150,000 / 1,000 = 150 X 8.44 = $1,266

Sales Price / 1,000 = #1000's X Factor = Monthly Payment

Use this worksheet to estimate the monthly mortgage payment on a 15-year loan compared to a 30-year loan.

NOTES

This worksheet helps you decide whether or not it would make sense to refinance your current mortgage to a lower-interest loan.

Should I Refinance?

Current principal and interest payment (not including taxes & insurance) ______________

New principal and interest payment – ______________

Equals monthly savings = ______________

______________ / ______________ = ______________

Total closing costs divided by savings = Number of months to break even

Example: Refinance on a $150,000 Mortgage at 8% to 6.5%

$1,434 current payment - $1,307 new payment = $127 savings

$2,300 closing cost divided by $127 savings = 18 months

Will you stay in your home longer than the number of months to break even? If so, you are a candidate for a refinance.

ESTIMATED CLOSING COSTS TABLE

Loan Amount	Closing Costs	Loan Amount	Closing Costs
30,000	1,500	75,000	1,850
35,000	1,550	80,000	1,900
40,000	1,600	85,000	1,925
45,000	1,650	90,000	1,950
50,000	1,700	95,000	1,975
55,000	1,725	100,000	2,000
60,000	1,775	150,000	2,300
65,000	1,800	200,000	2,600
70,000	1,825	250,000	2,900

How to Figure the Change in Your ARM

Your Adjustable Rate Mortgage (ARM) adjusts based on the movement of an index. You can find your index in your original note or mortgage. The most commonly used index is the Treasury Bill (T-Bill). The one-year ARM uses the one-year T-Bill, the three-year ARM uses the three-year T-Bill, and so on. Other commonly used indexes are the LIBOR and the 11th District Cost of Funds.

First, find out what index you use and when it is adjusted.

Next, find out (also from your loan paperwork) what margin was assigned to your loan (usually 2.59).

Basically, your ARM adjusts as the index moves.

The index is usually published daily in the *Wall Street Journal.*

So, if you have a one-year ARM that adjusts with the one-year T-Bill and a margin of 2.59 (which is typical), then, at the one-year anniversary of your closing, you would look up the one-year T-Bill in the *Wall Street Journal.* Add the T-Bill to your margin and you have your new rate (if it is not capped).

Example: T-Bill 4.41 plus margin 2.59 = 7% new interest rate.

Warning: Almost all ARMs start below margin the first year, guaranteeing a payment increase at anniversary unless rates DROP.

NOTES

Answer Key

Early	Survey	Homes	Tax
Retailer	MLS	Timeshares	Conventional
Enormous	Bottom	Hate	Private
Curb	Location	100%	FHA
Internet	Location	Renting	3%
More	Location	Patience	More
Multiple	Water	25%	VA
Friendships	View	15-year	Better
Relatives	Overlooking	10%	Owner
Interview	Street	High	Great
Warranty	Floorplan	Transfer	
Forced	Home	Borrower	
Inflation	Inspector	Interest	
Tax	Opinion	Only	
Free	Trailers	Reverse	
Unclean	Mobile	Accelerated	

Set Your Goals for the Week / Gazelle Focus

I will create a written, long-term plan for my real estate goals by this date:

Also this week, I am going to . . .

Review of Last Week

1. What are some specific ways in which your unique personality style impacts your work life?
2. Discuss the three-year professional plan you outlined for yourself last week.
3. Why is sacrifice so important in taking on a part-time job for short-term goals?
4. Recite all seven Baby Steps.

Small Group Discussion and Accountability

1. What does it mean to be "house poor"? Is anyone here in that situation?
2. Is it ever okay to rent for a while? Why or why not?
3. Have you ever been late on a mortgage payment? If so, how did that make you feel?
4. What are the dangers in 30-year mortgages, adjustable rate loans, and home equity loans?
5. If you have to take out a mortgage, what guidelines does Dave recommend? According to those principles, how much house can you actually afford?
6. How would paying off your home early make you feel? How would it affect your retirement?

Homework

1. **Complete your final Financial Snapshot,** either online or on the paper form included with this workbook.
2. **Plan a graduation party for next week!** Work with your other class members to create a celebration to remember!
3. ***Financial Peace Revisited*:** Read the subtitled sections "Real Estate Bargains" and "Owner Financing Bonanza" in chapter 13.

online resources™

Be sure to check out the special online features for this week.

- **Easy Payoff Calculator:** See how quickly you can pay off your mortgage!
- **Mortgage Calculator:** Find out how much house you can actually afford.
- **Get Help:** Ready to buy or sell a home? Find a local realtor with the heart of a teacher. If you need help, you can contact one of Dave's Endorsed Local Providers in your area.
- **Check Your Math:** Learn why it's a bad idea to keep a mortgage just for a tax deduction.

Dave Ramsey's Financial Peace® University

The Great Misunderstanding™

Unleashing the Power of Generous Giving

"The earth is the LORD's and the fullness thereof."

– Psalm 24:1 (KJV)

"You can't shake hands with a clenched fist."

– Golda Mier

"There are men who gain from their wealth only the fear of losing it."

– Antoine Riveroli

"Surplus wealth is a sacred trust to be managed for the good of others."

– Andrew Carnegie

Baby Step 7™

Build wealth and ___________!

You can do everything we teach and you will prosper, but if you don't understand this lesson, you will never have

___________ ___________.

The Great Misunderstanding, the paradox, is the mistaken belief that the way to have ________ is to hold on ______________.

Owners and Managers

You and I are asset _______________ for the ___________, so if we view it properly, we aren't giving our own money, anyway.

A ______________ is a manager, not an ____________.

Why does God tell us to _______ so often?

Giving makes us more __________-like; a spiritually mature Christian gives.

Giving moves you to become less ___________, and less selfish people have more of a tendency to _______________ in relationships and in wealth.

Because we are designed in God's image, we are happiest and most fulfilled when ______________ and _______________.

Why Give?

Giving is:

1. A _________________ of ___________________
2. __________________ and _________________
3. __________________ ____________________

Instructions for Giving

The tithe is a tenth (10%) of your ____________.

The Bible says to give first fruits, meaning off the __________.

The tithe is to go to your _______ ________, which provides the same function as the Old Testament _________________.

________________ are different than the tithe. They are __________ the tithe and are freely given from ____________.

"God loves a cheerful giver."

– 2 Corinthians 9:7 (NKJV)

"'And I will rebuke the devourer for your sakes, so that he will not destroy the fruit of your ground, nor shall the vine fail to bear fruit for you in the field,' says the Lord of hosts."

– Malachi 3:11 (NKJV)

"Every survivor, at whatever place he may live, let the men of that place support him with silver and gold, with goods and cattle, together with a freewill offering for the house of God which is in Jerusalem."

– Ezra 1:4 (NASB)

NOTES

The tithe is ____________.

The tithe is __________ __________________.

Never give with the _____________ of having your giving ________________.

Financial Peace is more than just God's system for understanding money, becoming debt free, and building wealth.

Financial Peace is when the Great Misunderstanding is _________________.

"When you have finished paying all the tithe of your increase..."

– Deuteronomy 26:12 (NASB)

"This stone, which I have set up as a pillar, will be God's house, and of all that you give me I will surely give a tenth to you."

– Genesis 28:22 (NASB)

"Woe to you, teachers of the law and Pharisees, you hypocrites! You give a tenth of your spices —mint, dill and cummin. But you have neglected the more important matters of the law—justice, mercy and faithfulness. You should have practiced the latter, without neglecting the former."

– Matthew 23:23 (NIV)

"And if I give all my possessions to feed the poor,
and if I surrender my body to be burned,
but do not have love, it profits me nothing."
1 Corinthians 13:3 (NASB)

"And all the tithe of the land, whether of the seed of the land
or of the fruit of the tree, is the LORD's. It is holy to the LORD."
Leviticus 27:30 (NKJV)

"You shall truly tithe all the increase of your grain
that the field produces year by year."
Deuteronomy 14:22 (NKJV)

"'Bring all the tithes into the storehouse, that there may be food in
My house, and try Me now in this,' says the LORD of hosts,

'If I will not open for you the windows of heaven and pour out for
you such blessing that there will not be room enough to receive it.'"
Malachi 3:10 (NKJV)

online

Give Financial Peace to others! Go online to find out how you can bring the message of freedom to other families.

NOTES

Answer Key

Give
Financial
Peace
More
Tightly
Managers
Lord
Steward
Owner
Give
Christ
Selfish

Prosper
Serving
Giving
Reminder
Ownership
Praise
Worship
Spiritual
Warfare
Increase
Top
Local

Church
Storehouse
Offerings
Above
Surplus
Pre-law
New Testament
Motive
Returned
Understood

Set Your Goals for the Week / Gazelle Focus

From now on, I will always have a household budget done by the first of each month.

Also this week, I am going to . . .

Review of Last Week

1. Homes in good neighborhoods appreciate and are priced on what three standards?
2. True or False: The time and money you spend fixing up your house prior to selling can greatly increase your asking price.
3. According to Financial Peace principles, is it wiser to buy a little less house with a 15-year mortgage or more house with a 30-year mortgage?
4. Which is better, an adjustable or fixed-rate mortgage?

Small Group Discussion and Accountability

1. Why don't we give as much as we'd like to at times?
2. How do you feel when you give?
3. Has anyone ever surprised you with a meaningful act of giving? How did that make you feel?
4. Why is it important to give while paying off debts?
5. How does viewing yourself as a manager of God's resources affect your thinking and behavior about money?
6. What's the most important lesson you've learned in FPU?
7. In what ways has your life changed as a result of getting your money under control?
8. Have the spiritual principles of this program helped you seek God and His will for your life?

Don't Forget!

1. **Financial Snapshots:** If you have done your snapshots on paper, be sure to turn the form in to your class coordinator. If you've done them online, make sure all four snapshots are complete!
2. **Testimonial Survey:** Complete the Testimonial Survey form on the page 179 and leave it with your coordinator.
3. **Start a new class:** Want to share what you've learned with others? Then start a new class in your area! Complete the Coordinator Application or call us at 888.22.PEACE (73223).

online resources™

Be sure to check out the special online features for this week.

- **Share It!** Find out how you can personally impact others who desperately need Financial Peace in their lives.
- **From Welfare to Independence:** Check out this inspiring two-minute mini-documentary about one woman's struggle for financial freedom.
- **My Total Money Makeover:** Take your money makeover to the next level and continue to enjoy our online money tools with our exciting online community, My Total Money Makeover!
- **Start a Class:** Learn how to start a new FPU class in your area!

COORDINATOR APPLICATION

Dave Ramsey's Financial Peace UNIVERSITY

Would you like to HELP CHANGE YOUR COMMUNITY by coordinating a class? Visit daveramsey.com/fpumember today to learn more about how you can become a volunteer coordinator!

daveramsey.com
phone: 888.22.PEACE
fax:615-371-5007

PERSONAL INFORMATION

FIRST NAME

LAST NAME

MAILING ADDRESS

CITY

STATE

ZIP CODE

EMAIL ADDRESS

DAYTIME PHONE NUMBER

The Lampo Group, Inc. is not a multi-level, insurance or investment based company. Are you currently involved in any of those three fields of work? O YES O NO

PLEASE SELECT YOUR LEVEL OF INTEREST:

- O I am gathering information now.
- O I plan on starting Financial Peace University.
- O I plan to start Financial Peace University in the next month.

OTHER AREAS OF INTEREST:

- O I am interested in becoming one of Dave's Certified Counselors. . .
  - O For Profit O Ministry
- O Curriculum for youth groups and high school students.

Please provide type of organization and organizational information you would like to coordinate for

TYPE OF ORGANIZATION:

- O Church
- O Community/University/College
- O Hispanic Group
- O High School Students
- O Literacy Program/Nonprofit Org
- O Military
- O Workplace
- O Youth Group

ORGANIZATION NAME

ADDRESS

CITY

STATE

ZIP CODE

PHONE NUMBER

WEBSITE

TYPE OF ORGANIZATION:

- O Church
- O Community/University/College
- O Hispanic Group
- O High School Students
- O Literacy Program/Nonprofit Org
- O Military
- O Workplace
- O Youth Group

ORGANIZATION NAME

ADDRESS

CITY

STATE

ZIP CODE

PHONE NUMBER

WEBSITE

TESTIMONIAL SURVEY

Dave Ramsey's Financial Peace UNIVERSITY

Please take a few minutes to share your comments about FPU.
To save time, you may choose to complete your survey ONLINE!
Go to daveramsey.com/fpumember today!

CLASS LOCATION CODE

CLASS START DATE (MM/DD/YY)

COORDINATOR FIRST NAME

COORDINATOR LAST NAME

How did you hear about Financial Peace University?

- O Family
- O Website
- O FPU Member
- O The Dave Ramsey Show
- O Friend
- O Live Event
- O Television
- O Radio Commercials
- O Newspaper
- O Coordinator
- O Church Bulletin
- O Bookstore
- O Other

How would you rate your situation when you started FPU?

O 1 O 2 O 3 O 4 O 5 O 6 O 7 O 8 O 9 O 10

Financially distressed — Financially secure

Overall, how well do you feel FPU has helped you improve your financial self-confidence, peace of mind, and sense of security, compared to your personal financial life before attending FPU?

O 1 O 2 O 3 O 4 O 5 O 6 O 7 O 8 O 9 O 10

Little Improvement — Big Improvement

Can you better manage your money now as a result of attending FPU? O Yes O No

Do you feel you would benefit from a one-on-one counseling session? O Yes O No

How much debt have you been able to PAY OFF since you first learned of the Financial Peace principles? $ .00

How much money have you been able to SAVE since you started applying the Financial Peace principles?

Emergency Fund $ .00

Total $ .00

Which lesson or lessons were the most beneficial and helpful to you?

How much impact has this program had on your personal relationships?

O 1 O 2 O 3 O 4 O 5 O 6 O 7 O 8 O 9 O 10

Little — Greatly

What has Financial Peace University done for you? (Please Print)

How would you rate your volunteer Coordinator?

O 1 O 2 O 3 O 4 O 5 O 6 O 7 O 8 O 9 O 10

Needs Improvement — Excellent

FPU Membership Information

FIRST NAME

LAST NAME

ADDRESS

CITY

STATE

ZIP CODE

PRIMARY PHONE

EMAIL ADDRESS

Are you interested in becoming involved as an FPU Coordinator or Group Leader?

- O At the location where I attended FPU
- O At my organization (church, business, etc...)

Please list organization name and city here:

AGE

O <18 O 18-25 O 26-35 O 36-45 O 46-55 O 56-65 O 65+

MARITAL STATUS

O Single O Married O Divorced O Widowed

RACE

O Caucasian O African-American O Hispanic O Asian O Other________________

SIZE OF FAMILY O 1 O 2 O 3 O 4 O 5 O 6+

REGULAR CHURCH ATTENDANCE O Yes O No

HOUSEHOLD INCOME

O <15,000 O 15,000-30,000 O 31,000-50,000 O 51,000-80,000 O 81,000-100,000 O 100,000+

COLLEGE

O Yes O No

INTERNET USER

O Yes O No

BUSINESS OWNER

O Yes O No

PAST BANKRUPTCY

O Yes O No

Recommendations For Financial Peace University

If you believe your employer, company or church would be interested in setting up the Financial Peace University program for the employees or church members, please list the person for us to contact.

CHURCH OR COMPANY NAME

CONTACT - FIRST NAME

CONTACT - LAST NAME

EMAIL ADDRESS

If you believe that the FPU program, or a one-on-one counseling session, would benefit your friends, family members, co-workers, etc., please fill in the information below so we can email them information about our program.

FIRST NAME

LAST NAME

EMAIL ADDRESS

FIRST NAME

LAST NAME

EMAIL ADDRESS

Dave Ramsey's Financial Peace University

Frequently Asked Questions

1. **How often can I go back through the FPU class after I graduate?**

   FPU members enjoy a lifetime membership to *Financial Peace University*. That means you can go back through the class as often as you wish! You can find a class in your area at daveramsey.com/fpu. You can attend a class without buying new materials. Simply use your existing membership kit for each new class you join.

2. **What is the Member Resource Center?**

   The FPU Member Resource Center (MRC) is a fantastic online resource that provides you with additional tools, content, and special features as you work through *Financial Peace University*. Each week of your 13-week class, the MRC offers you fresh insights on the FPU lessons, helpful reminders and budget tips, encouraging testimonies, and MRC-only special offers. Plus, you'll have access to these powerful features:

   - Online budget software to simplify your monthly cash flow plan, debt snowball, expense tracking, and more!
   - Exclusive, interactive teaching videos that bring clarity to the FPU concepts by showing you exactly how to apply them to your life!
   - Community message forums, where you can interact with other FPU members around the world!
   - Online Financial Snapshot form to help track your progress through the 13-week class!
   - Downloadable versions of all the budget forms used throughout FPU!
   - Extensive interactive glossary that demystifies hundreds of financial terms and concepts!
   - Up-to-date statistics and geographical information!
   - Regular contests and giveaways!

3. **How long will I have access to the Member Resource Center?**

   As an FPU member, you have complete access to all of the wonderful resources of the MRC for 15 weeks, which easily takes you throughout your first FPU class experience. After 15 weeks, you will still have access to the teaching content and lesson-related material. Plus, you will have the opportunity to continue accessing the online budget tools through the optional upgrade to our My Total Money Makeover community.

4. **How do I join the Member Resource Center?**

   It's easy! Simply get your FPU class code from your class coordinator and go to daveramsey.com/fpumember. Click the "Get Started Now" button on the homepage and follow the onscreen instructions, entering your class code when prompted.

   If you are participating in the FPU Home Study option, you will not have a class code. In this case, simply click "Get Started Now" and then and follow the appropriate instructions for registration without a class code.

5. **What is My Total Money Makeover (MyTMMO)? Do I get a discount?**

   MyTMMO takes your MRC experience to the next level with even more exclusive online tools! MyTMMO members have ongoing access to our online budget tools and a passionate community with active message forums and live chats. MyTMMO will walk with you through the Baby Steps, tracking your progress, offering encouragement and support, and celebrating your victories. Plus, MyTMMO members can download or podcast all three hours of *The Dave Ramsey Show* in CD-quality, commercial-free mp3 every day!

   Want a discount? No problem! As an FPU member, you'll get 25% off the yearly membership price to MyTMMO! You'll find more details and learn how to join MyTMMO in the Member Resource Center. If you enjoyed the MRC during FPU, you'll love My Total Money Makeover! Visit daveramsey.com and click on My Total Money Makeover.

6. **As an FPU member, do I get a special discount on Dave's live events, such as The Total Money Makeover LIVE or EntreLeadership?**

   Financial Peace University members are not eligible for live event discounts.

7. **Can I call the FPU office and get free help with my budget?**

   We've packed a ton of on-demand resources into the Member Resource Center, My Total Money Makeover, and daveramsey.com. There's a good chance you'll find an answer to your question there. Because of the sheer volume of FPU members, we simply cannot offer free one-on-one counseling over the phone. We do, however, have several options available, including connecting you with a trained financial counselor in your area. You can learn about our counseling services at daveramsey.com/counseling.

8. **Can I come to your office for one-on-one financial counseling?**

   Yes! You can schedule a personal, fee-based counseling session at our Brentwood, Tennessee office by calling 888.22.PEACE or emailing counseling@daveramsey.com. You can also find a counselor who has been personally trained by Dave's team at daveramsey.com/counseling.

9. **Can I order multiple copies of the FPU CD and DVD libraries or workbooks?**

   No. We make these resources available only to current FPU students or former graduates for review purposes only. These materials should not be distributed outside of an FPU class environment or used for any purpose beyond the individual FPU member's personal review.

10. **I want to share FPU with someone! Is it okay to bring a friend with me to a class session?**

    Yes! Feel free to bring a friend with you to one FPU session. You may want to tell your class coordinator ahead of time. Bring a different friend to each session if you would like.

11. How can I start a new class in my community, church, or workplace?

To start a new class, call 888.22.PEACE or visit daveramsey.com/fpu. You can also ask your class coordinator for the personal contact information of your class' current FPU Advisor.

12. I missed a class! What do I do?

If you missed a class, ask your class coordinator if he or she can review the lesson with you. Or, you can make it up by attending that same lesson in another local class. Find a class in your area at daveramsey.com/fpu. Also, your FPU membership kit contains an audio CD library of all 13 lessons in their entirety for your review.

13. My audio CDs, DVDs, or member workbook are damaged. Can I get a replacement?

If you received defective merchandise, we'll be glad to take care of that for you. Just call our Customer Care Center at 888.22.PEACE.

14. Does *Financial Peace University* come with a money-back guarantee?

We have a clear, simple, and easy-to-understand guarantee for our program:

If you do it, it works.

If you don't do it, it won't work!

If you will work the program, you won't want your money back.

If you don't work the program, you don't get your money back!

Dave Ramsey's Financial Peace University

Glossary

401(k): defined contribution plan offered by a corporation to its employees, which allows employees to set aside tax-deferred income for retirement purposes; in some cases, employers will match their contributions.

403(b): retirement plan similar to a 401(k) plan, but one that is offered by non-profit organizations, such as universities and some charitable organizations, rather than corporations; employees set aside tax-deferred dollars.

457 plan: non-qualified, deferred compensation plan established by state and local governments for tax-exempt government agencies, and tax-exempt employers, eligible employees are allowed to make salary deferral contributions to the 457 plan; earnings grow on a tax-deferred basis and contributions are not taxed until the assets are distributed from the plan.

529 plan: college savings plan that allows individuals to save on a tax-deferred basis in order to fund future college and graduate school expenses of a child or beneficiary; generally sponsored by a state, these are professionally managed investments.

Adjustable Rate Mortgage (ARM): home loan secured by a deed of trust or mortgage in which the interest rate will change periodically (i.e. annually); typically adjusted based on a published index such as the Treasury Bill or LIBOR; brought on as a result of high interest rates in the early 1980s as a way for banks to transfer the risk of higher interest rates to the consumer.

Aggressive Growth Stock Mutual Fund: mutual fund that seeks to provide maximum long-term capital growth from stocks of primarily smaller companies or narrow market segments; dividend income is incidental; the most volatile fund; also referred to as a small-cap fund.

Amortization Table: breakdown showing how much of each regular payment will be applied toward principal and how much toward interest over the life of a loan; also shows the gradual decrease of the loan balance until it reaches zero.

Annuity: contract sold by an insurance company, designed to provide payments to the holder at specified intervals, usually after retirement; the holder is taxed at the time of distribution or withdrawal, making this a tax-deferred arrangement.

Annual Percentage Rate (APR): cost of borrowing money on an annual basis; takes into account the interest rate and other related fees on a loan.

Asset: anything that is owned by an individual; with respect to saving and investing, assets are generally categorized as liquid (cash) and capital (investment) assets.

Back-End Load: sales commission paid when the investor sells mutual fund shares; sometimes phased out over several years; also called redemption fee or contingent-deferred sales charge.

Balanced Fund: mutual fund that invests in more than one type of financial asset: stocks, bonds, and in some cases, cash investments.

Balloon Mortgage: home loan in which the sum of the monthly payments is insufficient to repay the entire loan; a final payment comes due, which is a lump sum of the remaining principal balance.

Bankruptcy: legal procedure for dealing with debt problems of individuals and businesses; specifically, a legal court case filed under one of the chapters of Title 11 of the United States Code (also see Chapter 7 bankruptcy, Chapter 11 bankruptcy, and Chapter 13 bankruptcy).

Bond: debt instrument where an issuer such as a corporation, municipality, or government agency owes you money; a form of I.O.U.; the issuer makes regular interest payments on the bond and promises to pay back or redeem the face value of the bond, at a specified point in the future (the maturity date).

Break-Even Analysis: method used to evaluate the wisdom of a financial decision by determining the length of time it will take for cost of the decision to be recouped.

Budget: cash flow plan; assigns every dollar to a specific category/expense the beginning of each month.

Cash Value Insurance: also known as permanent life insurance; premiums include a death benefit and plan to build savings within the policy; two main types are whole life and universal life; significantly more expensive than term life insurance.

C.D.: Certificate of Deposit, usually at a bank; savings account with a slightly higher interest rate because of a longer savings commitment (i.e. six months, one year, etc.).

Chapter 7 Bankruptcy: chapter of the Bankruptcy Code providing for liquidation of the debtor's assets in order to repay the creditors; certain assets or aggregate value of assets of the debtor may be exempt based on state law.

Chapter 11 Bankruptcy: reorganization bankruptcy, usually involving a corporation or partnership; generally includes a plan of reorganization to keep a business alive and pay creditors over time.

Chapter 13 Bankruptcy: chapter of the Bankruptcy Code providing for an individual to repay debts over time, usually three to five years; debtor makes periodic payments to the bankruptcy trustee, who in turn pays the creditors; sometimes includes adjustments to debt balances within the bankruptcy.

Check Card: type of card, often bearing the seal of a major credit card company, issued by a bank and used to make purchases; unlike a credit card, the money comes directly out of a checking account; also called debit card.

Collision: portion of auto insurance that covers losses due to vehicle damage in an accident.

Compound Interest: interest paid on interest previously earned; credited daily, monthly, quarterly, semi-annually, or annually on both principal and previously credited interest.

Contents Policy: insurance policy that covers your possessions in a home or apartment; sometimes called "renter's insurance."

Conventional Loan: mortgage obtained through the Federal National Mortgage Association (FNMA), which insures against default; generally includes a down payment of 5-20% or more.

Cosigning: offering to guarantee someone else's loan; responsible for loan repayment if the borrower defaults.

Credit Laws:

- **Fair Credit Reporting Act (1971):** federal law governing the reporting of debt repayment information; establishes when a credit reporting agency may provide a report to someone; states that obsolete information must be taken off (seven to 10 years); gives consumers the right to know what is in their credit report; requires that both a credit bureau and information provider (i.e. department store) have an obligation to correct wrong information; gives consumers the right to dispute inaccurate information and add a 100-word statement to their report to explain accurate negative information; gives consumers the right to know what credit bureau provided the report when they are turned down for credit.

- **Fair Credit Billing Act (1975):** federal law that covers credit card billing problems and applies to all open-end credit accounts (i.e. credit cards and overdraft checking); states that consumers should send a written billing error notice to the creditor within 60 days (after receipt of first bill containing an error), which the creditor must acknowledge in 30 days; requires the creditor to investigate and prohibits them from damaging a consumer's credit rating while a dispute is pending.
- **Fair Debt Collection Practices Act (1978):** federal law that prohibits debt collectors from engaging in unfair, deceptive, or abusive practices when collecting debts; requires collectors to send a written notice stating the name of the creditor and the amount owed; prohibits contacting the consumer if he or she disputes in writing within 30 days (unless collector furnishes proof of the debt); requires collectors to identify themselves on the phone and limits calls to between 8:00 a.m. and 9:00 p.m. unless the consumer agrees to another time; prohibits calling the consumer at work if requested.
- **Equal Credit Opportunity Act (1975):** federal law that ensures consumers are given an equal chance to receive credit; prohibits discrimination on the basis of gender, race, marital status, religion, national origin, age, or receipt of public assistance; prohibits lenders from asking about plans to have children or refusing to consider consistently received alimony or child support payments as income; grants the consumer legal rights to know why he or she was denied credit.
- **Truth in Lending Act (1969):** federal law that mandates disclosure of information about the cost of credit; mandates that the finance charge (i.e. all charges to borrow money, including interest) and the annual percentage rate (APR) must be displayed prominently on forms and statements used by creditors; provides criminal penalties for willful violators, as well as civil remedies; protects against unauthorized use of one's credit card, limiting personal loss to $50 if the card is lost or stolen.
- **Fair Credit and Charge Card Disclosure Act (1989):** portion of the Truth in Lending Act that mandates a section on credit card applications that describes key features and cost (i.e. APR, grace period for purchases, minimum finance charge, balance calculation method, annual fees, transaction fees for cash advances, and penalty fees such as over the limit fees and late payment fees).

Debit Card: see Check Card.

Debt Consolidation: act of combining all debts into one monthly payment, typically extending the terms and the length of time required to repay the debt.

Debt Snowball: preferred method of debt repayment; includes a list of all debts organized from smallest to largest balance; minimum payments are made to all debts except for the smallest, which is attacked with the largest possible payments.

Deductible: amount you have to pay out-of-pocket for expenses before the insurance company will begin contributing to cover all or a portion of the remaining costs.

Direct Transfer: movement of tax-deferred retirement plan money from one qualified plan or custodian to another; results in no immediate tax liabilities or penalties, but requires IRS reporting.

Disability Insurance: policy that insures a worker in the event of an occupational mishap resulting in disability; compensates the injured worker for lost pay.

Diversification: to spread around one's investment dollars among several different classes of financial assets and among the securities of many issuers; results in lowered risk.

Dividend: distribution of a portion of a company's earnings, decided by the board of directors, to a class of its shareholders; generally distributed in the form of cash or stock.

Educational Savings Account (ESA): after-tax college fund that grows tax-free for educational uses; eligibility based on parents' annual income.

Elimination Period: amount of time that lapses after a disabling event and before the insurance company begins to pay benefits.

Emergency Fund: three to six months of expenses in readily available cash to be used only in the event of an emergency; Baby Step 3.

Envelope System: series of envelopes, divided into pre-determined categories, used to store cash for planned monthly expenses; self-imposed discipline tool to assist people in managing their monthly finances; possible categories include food, entertainment, gas, etc.

Equity: one's stake, or level of ownership, in an item of value.

Fixed Annuity: type of annuity that guarantees a certain rate of return; see annuity.

Forbearance: agreement between a lender and a debtor to "catch up" a past due account over a specified period of time; lender grants a postponement of loan payments for a set period of time, giving the borrower time to make up for overdue payments.

Foreclosure: process by which the holder of a mortgage seizes the property of a homeowner who has not made interest and/or principal payments on time as stipulated in the mortgage contract.

Front-End Load: sales commission that is paid up-front when shares of a mutual fund are purchased.

Garnishment: court-ordered settlement that allows a lender to take monies owed directly from a borrower's paycheck; only allowed as part of a court judgment.

Grace Period: time period during which a borrower can pay the full balance of credit due with no finance charges.

Growth and Income Mutual Fund: funds that buy stocks in larger, more established companies; contain medium-sized companies or growth stocks; also called a large-cap fund.

Growth Stock Mutual Fund: funds that buy stock in medium-sized companies that have experienced some growth and are still expanding; also called a mid-cap fund.

Home Equity Loan (HEL): credit line offered by mortgage lenders that allows a homeowner to borrow money against the equity in their home.

Homeowner's Insurance: policy that covers a loss due to damage, theft, or injury within one's home.

House Poor: condition of having a disproportionately high house payment that limits one's ability to maintain the home and/or meet necessities.

Individual Retirement Account/Arrangement (IRA): tax-deferred arrangement for individuals with earned income and their non-income-producing spouses; growth is not taxed until money is withdrawn; contributions to an IRA are often tax-deductible.

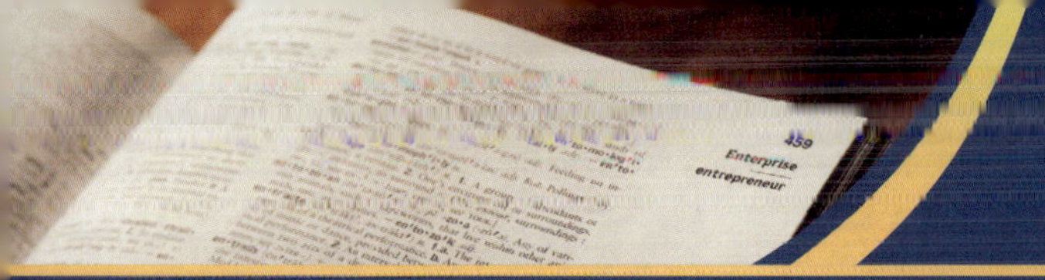

Inflation: rate at which the general level of prices for goods and services rises.

Interest: 1) charge for borrowed money generally defined as a percentage. 2) money paid to savers and investors by financial institutions, governments, or corporations for the use of their money (such as a 2% return on money held in a savings account).

Interest Rate: percentage paid to a lender for the use of borrowed money.

Internal Revenue Service (IRS): federal agency responsible for the collection of federal taxes, including personal and corporate, Social Security, and excise and gift taxes.

International Stock Mutual Fund: mutual fund that contains international or overseas companies.

Investment: account or arrangement in which one would put their money for long-term growth; should not be withdrawn for a suggested minimum of five years.

Large-Cap Fund: funds comprised of large, well-established companies.

Liability Insurance: policy that protects an individual in the event of a lawsuit due to injury on one's personal property or as the result of an automobile accident.

Life Insurance: type of insurance designed to replace income lost due to death; traditionally two types: term and cash value.

Liquidity: quality of an asset that permits it to be converted quickly into cash without loss of value; availability of money; as there is more liquidity, there is typically less return.

Load Fund: mutual fund that sells shares with a sales charge of typically 2-6% of the net amount indicated; some no-load funds also levy distribution fees permitted by Article 12b-1 of the Investment Company Act; these are typically 0.25%; a true no-load fund has no sales charge.

Loan To Value (LTV): value of a property versus the amount borrowed against it; Example: a 70/30 LTV means that the property owner owes 70% of the item's worth and owns 30% of the item's worth.

Long-Term Care Insurance: policy that covers the cost of nursing home or in-home care insurance; recommended for everyone over age 60.

Low-Load Fund: mutual fund that charges a sales commission equal to 3% or less of the amount invested.

Medicare: federal government program of transfer payments for certain health care expenses for citizens 65 or older; managed by the Social Security Administration.

Mid-Cap Fund: mutual fund containing a group of medium-sized companies that are growing.

Money Market Fund: mutual fund that seeks to maintain a stable share price and to earn current income by investing in interest-bearing instruments with short-term (usually 90 days or less) maturities.

Mortgage: loan secured by the collateral of some specified real estate property, which obligates the borrower to make a predetermined series of payments.

Mortgage Life Insurance: insurance policy that pays off the remaining balance of the insured person's mortgage at death.

Multiple Listings Service (MLS): computer program used by realtors to search frequently updated listings of available properties in order to find prospective homes for their clients.

Mutual Fund: pool of money managed by an investment company and invested in multiple companies, bonds, etc.; offers investors a variety of goals, depending on the fund and its investment charter; often used to generate income on a regular basis or to preserve an investor's money; sometimes used to invest in companies that are growing at a rapid pace.

Nest Egg: sum of money earmarked for ongoing living expenses at retirement or when employment income otherwise stops.

No-Load Mutual Fund: open-ended investment company whose shares are sold without a sales charge; might include other distribution charges, such as Article 12b-1 fees, but a true no-load fund has neither a sales charge nor a distribution fee.

Occupational Disability: type of insurance that provides an income in case the insured becomes unable to perform the job he/she was educated or trained to do.

Owner Financing: type of home loan in which the existing owner acts as the mortgage holder; payments are made to the owner, rather than to a mortgage company or bank.

Payroll Deduction: amount subtracted from a paycheck, either by government requirement (mandatory taxes, Social Security, etc.) or at the employee's request (health insurance, retirement plan, etc.).

Preauthorized Checking (PAC): system of automatic payment processing by which bills, deposits, and payments are handled electronically and at regular intervals or on a predetermined schedule.

Premium: amount you pay monthly, quarterly, semi-annually, or annually to purchase different types of insurance.

Principal: original amount of money invested, excluding any interest or dividends; also called the face value of a loan, excluding interest.

Private Mortgage Insurance (PMI): policy paid by the mortgage borrower that protects the lender against loss resulting from default on a mortgage loan.

Pro Rata: debt repayment plan by which the borrower repays each lender a fair percentage of the total debt owed when one cannot make the minimum payments on a debt.

Prospectus: official document that contains information required by the Securities and Exchange Commission to describe a mutual fund.

Rate of Return: return on an investment expressed as a percentage of its cost; also called yield.

Renter's Insurance: see Contents Insurance.

Replacement Cost: insurance that pays the actual cost of replacing your home and its contents after a catastrophic event.

Risk: degree of uncertainty of return on an asset; in business, the likelihood of loss or reduced profit.

Risk Return Ratio: relationship of substantial reward in comparison to the amount of risk taken.

Rollover: movement of funds from a tax-deferred retirement plan from one qualified plan or custodian to another; incurs no immediate tax liabilities or penalties, but requires IRS reporting.

Roth IRA: retirement account funded with after-tax dollars that subsequently grows tax free.

Roth 401(k): employer-sponsored retirement savings account that is funded with after-tax dollars and subsequently grows tax free.

Rule of 78: pre-payment penalty in a financing contract; the portion of a 90-days same-as-cash agreement that states that the entire loan amount plus the interest accumulated over the first 90 days becomes due immediately.

Savings Bond: certificate representing a debt; Example: U.S. savings bond is a loan to the government in which the government agrees to repay the amount borrowed, with interest, to the bondholder; government bonds are issued in face value denominations from $50 to $10,000 with local and state tax-free interest and semi-annually adjusted interest rates.

Self-Insured: condition of wealth at which time one no longer needs an outside insurance policy to cover a loss.

Share: piece of ownership in a company stock or mutual fund.

Short-Term Disability: minimal period of incapacitation; often used to describe an insurance policy that insures one's income for the immediate future following an incapacitating event.

Simple Interest: interest credited daily, monthly, quarterly, semi-annually, or annually on principal only, not previously credited interest.

Simple IRA: salary deduction plan for retirement benefits provided by some small companies with fewer than 100 employees.

Simplified Employee Pension Plan (SEPP): pension plan in which both the employee and the employer contribute to an individual retirement account; also available to the self-employed.

Small-Cap Fund: mutual fund that invests in companies whose market value is less than $1 billion; largely consists of smaller, more volatile companies; also called aggressive growth stock mutual fund.

Social Security: federal government program of transfer payments for retirement, disability, or the loss of income from a parent or guardian; funds come from a tax on income, which is a payroll deduction labeled FICA.

Stocks: securities that represent part ownership or equity in a corporation, wherein each share is a claim on its proportionate stake in the corporation's assets and profits, some of which may be paid out as dividends.

Stop-Loss: total out-of-pocket expense for health insurance; once reached, insurance will pay 100 percent.

Tax Deduction: expense that a taxpayer is allowed to deduct from taxable income; examples include money paid as home mortgage interest and charitable donations.

Tax-Deferred Income: dividends, interest, and unrealized capital gains on investments in a qualified account, such as a retirement plan, in which income is not subject to taxation until a withdrawal is made.

Tax Exemptions: amount that a taxpayer who meets certain criteria can subtract from a taxable income; see tax credit and tax deduction.

Term Insurance: life insurance coverage for a specified period of time.

Title Insurance: coverage that protects a policyholder from future challenges to the title claim of a property that may result in loss of the property.

Umbrella Liability Insurance: insurance policy that acts as a protective covering over your home and car against liability caused by an accident.

Uniform Gifts to Minors Act (UGMA): legislation that provides a tax-effective manner of transferring property to minors without the complications of trusts or guardianship restrictions.

Uniform Transfers to Minors Act (UTMA): law similar to the Uniform Gifts to Minors Act (UGMA) that extends the definition of gifts to include real estate, paintings, royalties, and patents.

Universal Life: type of life insurance policy, similar to cash value but with better projected returns.

VA Loan: type of mortgage loan designed to benefit veterans that allows for a true zero-down mortgage; generally more expensive than a conventional mortgage.

Value Fund: mutual fund that emphasizes stocks of companies whose growth prospects are generally regarded as sub-par by the market, resulting in value stocks typically priced below average in comparison with such factors as revenue, earnings, book value, and dividends.

Variable Annuity: annuity that has a varying rate of return based on the mutual funds in which one has invested; also see annuity.

Variable Life: type of life insurance that is similar to cash value, but buys into mutual funds to project better returns.

Viatical: contractual arrangement in which a business buys life insurance policies from terminally ill patients for a percentage of the face value.

Volatility: fluctuations in market value of a mutual fund or other security; the greater a fund's volatility, the wider the fluctuations between high and low prices.

Whole Life Insurance: type of insurance that contains a low-yield savings plan within the insurance policy; more expensive than term insurance.

Zero-Based Budget: cash flow plan that assigns an expense to every dollar of one's income, wherein the total income minus the total expenses equals zero.

Dave Ramsey's Financial Peace UNIVERSITY

Financial Forms

PERF HERE - DO NOT PRINT

The Basic Quickie Budget (Instructions)

This form will help you get your feet wet in the area of budgeting. It is only one page and should not be intimidating as you get started. The purpose of this form is to show you exactly how much money you need every month in order to survive. We won't get into the details of your credit card bills, student loans, and other consumer debts here. *This is just to give you a starting point as you begin to take control of your money.* You will learn how to create a full monthly cash flow plan in the third class session.

There are four columns on this form:

1. **Monthly Total**
   - This column shows you how much you are spending on necessities each month.
   - If you do not know the amount, write down your best estimate.
   - If an estimate is grossly inaccurate, then you may have never even noticed how much you were spending in that area before now. Don't beat yourself up about this!

2. **Payoff Total**
   - Write down how much money is required to completely pay off that item.
   - This line only appears in the relevant categories (mortgage, car debt, etc.)

3. **How Far Behind?**
   - If your account is past due in any category, write down how many days you are behind.
   - If you are up-to-date, simply write a zero or "N/A" (not applicable) here.

4. **Type of Account**
   - Write in how this area is paid—by check, automatic bank draft, cash, etc.
   - Early in the FPU course, you will see the benefits of using cash for certain items. Challenge yourself by identifying categories for which you can use cash only.
   - The asterisks (*) on the form indicate areas in which a cash-based approach could be helpful.

The Basic Quickie Budget

Item	Monthly Total	Payoff Total	How Far Behind	Type of Account
GIVING	______		______	______
SAVING	______		______	______
HOUSING				
First Mortgage	______	______	______	______
Second Mortgage	______	______	______	______
Repairs/Mn. Fee	______		______	______
UTILITIES				
Electricity	______		______	______
Water	______		______	______
Gas	______		______	______
Phone	______		______	______
Trash	______		______	______
Cable	______		______	______
*Food	______		______	______
TRANSPORTATION				
Car Payment	______	______	______	______
Car Payment	______	______	______	______
*Gas & Oil	______		______	______
*Repairs & Tires	______		______	______
Car Insurance	______		______	______
*CLOTHING	______		______	______
PERSONAL				
Disability Ins.	______		______	______
Health Insurance	______		______	______
Life Insurance	______		______	______
Child Care	______		______	______
*Entertainment	______		______	______
OTHER MISC.	______		______	______

TOTAL MONTHLY NECESSITIES ______

Major Components of a Healthy Financial Plan (Form 1)

	Action Needed	Action Date
Written Cash Flow Plan	____________________	__________
Will and/or Estate Plan	____________________	__________
Debt Reduction Plan	____________________	__________
Tax Reduction Plan	____________________	__________
Emergency Funding	____________________	__________
Retirement Funding	____________________	__________
College Funding	____________________	__________
Charitable Giving	____________________	__________
Teach My Children	____________________	__________
Life Insurance	____________________	__________
Health Insurance	____________________	__________
Disability Insurance	____________________	__________
Auto Insurance	____________________	__________
Homeowner's Insurance	____________________	__________

I (We) ______________________________, (a) responsible adult(s), do hereby promise to take the above stated actions by the above stated dates to financially secure the well-being of my (our) family and myself (ourselves).

Signed:____ Date:______________

Signed:____ Date:______________

Consumer Equity Sheet (Form 2)

ITEM / DESCRIBE	VALUE	–	DEBT	=	EQUITY
Real Estate ________	________		________		________
Real Estate ________	________		________		________
Car ________	________		________		________
Car ________	________		________		________
Cash On Hand	________		________		________
Checking Account	________		________		________
Checking Account	________		________		________
Savings Account	________		________		________
Savings Account	________		________		________
Money Market Account	________		________		________
Mutual Funds	________		________		________
Retirement Plan	________		________		________
Cash Value (Insurance)	________		________		________
Household Items	________		________		________
Jewelry			________		________
Antiques	________		________		________
Boat	________		________		________
Unsecured Debt (Neg)	________		________		________
Credit Card Debt (Neg)	________		________		________
Other ________	________		________		________
Other ________	________		________		________
Other ________	________		________		________
TOTAL	________		________		________

Extra copies of this form can be found online at **daveramsey.com/fpumember.**

PERF HERE - DO NOT PRINT

Income Sources (Form 3)

SOURCE	AMOUNT	PERIOD/DESCRIBE
Salary 1	______	______
Salary 2	______	______
Salary 3	______	______
Bonus	______	______
Self-Employment	______	______
Interest Income	______	______
Dividend Income	______	______
Royalty Income	______	______
Rents	______	______
Notes	______	______
Alimony	______	______
Child Support	______	______
AFDC	______	______
Unemployment	______	______
Social Security	______	______
Pension	______	______
Annuity	______	______
Disability Income	______	______
Cash Gifts	______	______
Trust Fund	______	______
Other______	______	______
Other______	______	______
Other______	______	______
TOTAL	______	

Lump Sum Payment Planning (Form 4)

Payments you make on a non-monthly basis, such as insurance premiums and taxes, can be budget busters if you do not plan for them every month. Therefore, you must annualize the cost and convert these to monthly budget items. That way, you can save the money each month and will not be caught off-guard when your bi-monthly, quarterly, semi-annual, or annual bills come due. Simply divide the annual cost by 12 to determine the monthly amount you should save for each item.

ITEM NEEDED	ANNUAL AMOUNT		MONTHLY AMOUNT
Real Estate Taxes	____________	/ 12 =	____________
Homeowner's Insurance	____________	/ 12 =	____________
Home Repairs	____________	/ 12 =	____________
Replace Furniture	____________	/ 12 =	____________
Medical Bills	____________	/ 12 =	____________
Health Insurance	____________	/ 12 =	____________
Life Insurance	____________	/ 12 =	____________
Disability Insurance	____________	/ 12 =	____________
Car Insurance	____________	/ 12 =	____________
Car Repair/Tags	____________	/ 12 =	____________
Replace Car	____________	/ 12 =	____________
Clothing	____________	/ 12 =	____________
Tuition	____________	/ 12 =	____________
Bank Note	____________	/ 12 =	____________
IRS (Self-Employed)	____________	/ 12 =	____________
Vacation	____________	/ 12 =	____________
Gifts (including Christmas)	____________	/ 12 =	____________
Other ____________	____________	/ 12 =	____________

PERF HERE - DO NOT PRINT

Monthly Cash Flow Plan (Instructions)

Every single dollar of your income should be allocated to some category on this form. When you're done, your total income minus expenses should equal zero. If it doesn't, then you need to adjust some categories (such as debt reduction, giving, or saving) so that it does equal zero. Use some common sense here, too. Do not leave things like clothes, car repairs, or home improvements off this list. If you don't plan for these things, then you're only setting yourself up for failure later.

Yes, this budget form is long. It's *really* long. We do that so that we can list practically every expense imaginable on this form to prevent you from forgetting something. Don't expect to put something on *every* line item. Just use the ones that are relevant to your specific situation.

Every main category on this form has subcategories. Fill in the monthly expense for each subcategory, and then write down the grand total for that category. Later, as you actually pay the bills and work through the month, use the "Actually Spent" column to record what you really spent in each area. If there is a substantial difference between what you budgeted and what you spent, then you'll need to readjust the budget to make up for the difference. If one category continually comes up over or short for two or three months, then you need to adjust the budgeted amount accordingly.

Use the "% Take Home Pay" column to record what percentage of your income actually goes to each category. Then, use the "Recommended Percentages" sheet (Form 6) to see if your percentages are in line with what we recommend.

Notes:

- An asterisk (*) beside an item indicates an area for which you should use the envelope system.
- The emergency fund should get all the savings until you've completed your full emergency fund of three to six months of expenses (Baby Step 3).
- Don't forget to include your annualized items from the "Lump Sum Payment Planning" sheet (Form 4), including your Christmas gift planning.

Monthly Cash Flow Plan (Form 5)

Budgeted Item	Sub Total	TOTAL	Actually Spent	% of Take Home Pay
CHARITABLE GIFTS	______	______	______	
SAVING				
Emergency Fund	______	______		
Retirement Fund	______	______		
College Fund	______	______	______	______
HOUSING				
First Mortgage	______	______		
Second Mortgage	______	______		
Real Estate Taxes	______	______		
Homeowner's Ins.	______	______		
Repairs or Mn. Fee	______	______		
Replace Furniture	______	______		
Other ________	______	______	______	______
UTILITIES				
Electricity	______		______	
Water	______		______	
Gas	______		______	
Phone	______		______	
Trash	______		______	
Cable	______	______	______	______
*FOOD				
*Grocery	______	______		
*Restaurants	______	______	______	______
TRANSPORTATION				
Car Payment	______	______		
Car Payment	______		______	
*Gas and Oil	______		______	
*Repairs and Tires	______		______	
Car Insurance	______		______	
License and Taxes	______		______	
Car Replacement	______	______	______	______
PAGE 1 TOTAL		______	______	

PERF HERE - DO NOT PRINT

Monthly Cash Flow Plan (Form 5 – continued)

Budgeted Item	Sub Total	TOTAL	Actually Spent	% of Take Home Pay
*CLOTHING				
*Children	______		______	
*Adults	______		______	
*Cleaning/Laundry	______	______	______	______
MEDICAL/HEALTH				
Disability Insurance	______		______	
Health Insurance	______		______	
Doctor Bills	______		______	
Dentist	______		______	
Optometrist	______		______	
Medications	______	______	______	______
PERSONAL				
Life Insurance	______		______	
Child Care	______		______	
*Baby Sitter	______		______	
*Toiletries	______		______	
*Cosmetics	______		______	
*Hair Care	______		______	
Education/Adult	______		______	
School Tuition	______		______	
School Supplies	______		______	
Child Support	______		______	
Alimony	______		______	
Subscriptions	______		______	
Organization Dues	______		______	
Gifts (incl. Christmas)	______		______	
Miscellaneous	______		______	
*Blow Money	______	______	______	______
PAGE 2 TOTAL		______		

Monthly Cash Flow Plan (Form 5 – continued)

Budgeted Item	Sub Total	TOTAL	Actually Spent	% of Take Home Pay
RECREATION				
*Entertainment	______		______	
Vacation			______	______
DEBTS (Hopefully -0-)				
Visa 1	______		______	
Visa 2	______		______	
Master Card 1	______		______	
Master Card 2	______		______	
American Express	______		______	
Discover Card	______		______	
Gas Card 1	______		______	
Gas Card 2	______		______	
Dept. Store Card 1	______		______	
Dept. Store Card 2	______		______	
Finance Co. 1	______		______	
Finance Co. 2	______		______	
Credit Line	______		______	
Student Loan 1	______		______	
Student Loan 2	______		______	
Other ______	______		______	
Other ______	______		______	
Other ______	______		______	
Other ______	______		______	
Other ______	______	______	______	______

PAGE 3 TOTAL	______	______
PAGE 2 TOTAL	______	______
PAGE 1 TOTAL	______	______
GRAND TOTAL	______	______
TOTAL HOUSEHOLD INCOME	______	
	ZERO	

Recommended Percentages (Form 6)

How much of your income should be spent on housing, giving, food, etc.? Through experience and research, we recommend the following percentages. However, you should remember that these are only *recommended* percentages. If you have an unusually high or low income, then these numbers could change dramatically. For example, if you have a high income, the *percentage* that is spent on food will be much lower than someone who earns half of that.

If you find that you spend much more in one category than we recommend, however, it may be necessary to adjust your lifestyle in that area in order to enjoy more freedom and flexibility across the board.

ITEM	ACTUAL %	RECOMMENDED %
CHARITABLE GIFTS	________	10 – 15%
SAVING	________	5 – 10%
HOUSING	________	25 – 35%
UTILITIES	________	5 – 10%
FOOD	________	5 – 15%
TRANSPORTATION	________	10 – 15%
CLOTHING	________	2 – 7%
MEDICAL/HEALTH	________	5 – 10%
PERSONAL	________	5 – 10%
RECREATION	________	5 – 10%
DEBTS	________	5 – 10%

PERF HERE - DO NOT PRINT

Allocated Spending Plan (Instructions)

Now that you've already planned out the entire month on the "Monthly Cash Flow Plan" (Form 5), let's get just a little bit more precise. On this form, you will allocate—or spend—all of your money from each individual pay period.

There are four columns on this form, representing the four weeks in a given month. You will use one column for each week you get paid. If you are married and your spouse earns an income, then you will both use this same form. For weeks in which you both receive a paycheck, simply add those two incomes together and use a single column. Be sure to write the pay date at the top of the column.

Now, go down the list and allocate each expense to a specific payday, using your bills' due dates as a guide. For example, if your phone bill is due on the 22nd and you get paid on the 15th and 30th, then you know that you would probably pay that bill from your income on the 15th. Some things, like utility bills, will be paid monthly, while other items, such as food and gasoline, could be weekly. The point here is to anticipate both your upcoming expenses and your upcoming income and plan accordingly.

Beside each line item, you'll see two blanks separated by a slash (/). Put the expense to the left of the slash and the remaining income from that pay period to the right of the slash. As you work your way down the column, the income remaining should diminish until you reach a perfect zero at the bottom of the list. If you have money left over at the end of the column, go back and adjust an area, such as savings or giving, so that you spend every single dollar.

This level of detail may be uncomfortable to you at first, but the payoff is worth it. By specifically "naming" every dollar before you actually get it in your hands, you will remove an incredible amount of stress and curb your overspending.

NOTES:

- If you have an irregular income, such as self-employment or commissions, you should use the "Irregular Income Planning" sheet (Form 8) instead of this "Allocated Spending Plan."

- If you know that you have an impulse spending problem, then you may want to allocate more money to the "Blow" category. That way, you are at least planning for it and setting up some boundaries for yourself.

- An asterisk (*) beside an item indicates an area for which you should use the envelope system.

Allocated Spending Plan (Form 7)

PAY PERIOD:	___/___	___/___	___/___	___/___
ITEM:				
INCOME	___/___	___/___	___/___	___/___
CHARITABLE	___/___	___/___	___/___	___/___
SAVING				
Emergency Fund	___/___	___/___	___/___	___/___
Retirement Fund	___/___	___/___	___/___	___/___
College Fund	___/___	___/___	___/___	___/___
HOUSING				
First Mortgage	___/___	___/___	___/___	___/___
Second Mortgage	___/___	___/___	___/___	___/___
Real Estate Taxes	___/___	___/___	___/___	___/___
Homeowner's Ins.	___/___	___/___	___/___	___/___
Repairs or Mn. Fees	___/___	___/___	___/___	___/___
Replace Furniture	___/___	___/___	___/___	___/___
Other _______	___/___	___/___	___/___	___/___
UTILITIES				
Electricity	___/___	___/___	___/___	___/___
Water	___/___	___/___	___/___	___/___
Gas	___/___	___/___	___/___	___/___
Phone	___/___	___/___	___/___	___/___
Trash	___/___	___/___	___/___	___/___
Cable	___/___	___/___	___/___	___/___
*FOOD				
*Grocery	___/___	___/___	___/___	___/___
*Restaurants	___/___	___/___	___/___	___/___

Allocated Spending Plan (Form 7 – continued)

TRANSPORTATION				
Car Payment	____/____	____/____	____/____	____/____
Car Payment	____/____	____/____	____/____	____/____
*Gas and Oil	____/____	____/____	____/____	____/____
*Repairs and Tires	____/____	____/____	____/____	____/____
Car Insurance	____/____	____/____	____/____	____/____
License and Taxes	____/____	____/____	____/____	____/____
Car Replacement	____/____	____/____	____/____	____/____
*CLOTHING				
*Children	____/____	____/____	____/____	____/____
*Adults	____/____	____/____	____/____	____/____
*Cleaning/Laundry	____/____	____/____	____/____	____/____
MEDICAL/HEALTH				
Disability Insurance	____/____	____/____	____/____	____/____
Health Insurance	____/____	____/____	____/____	____/____
Doctor	____/____	____/____	____/____	____/____
Dentist	____/____	____/____	____/____	____/____
Optometrist	____/____	____/____	____/____	____/____
Medications	____/____	____/____	____/____	____/____
PERSONAL				
Life Insurance	____/____	____/____	____/____	____/____
Child Care	____/____	____/____	____/____	____/____
*Baby Sitter	____/____	____/____	____/____	____/____
*Toiletries	____/____	____/____	____/____	____/____
*Cosmetics	____/____	____/____	____/____	____/____
*Hair Care	____/____	____/____	____/____	____/____
Education/Adult	____/____	____/____	____/____	____/____
School Tuition	____/____	____/____	____/____	____/____
School Supplies	____/____	____/____	____/____	____/____
Child Support	____/____	____/____	____/____	____/____

Allocated Spending Plan (Form / – continued)

Alimony	___/___	___/___	___/___	___/___
Subscriptions	___/___	___/___	___/___	___/___
Organization Dues	___/___	___/___	___/___	___/___
Gifts (including Christmas)	___/___	___/___	___/___	___/___
Miscellaneous	___/___	___/___	___/___	___/___
*BLOW $$	___/___	___/___	___/___	___/___
RECREATION				
*Entertainment	___/___	___/___	___/___	___/___
Vacation	___/___	___/___	___/___	___/___
DEBTS (Hopefully -0-)				
Visa 1	___/___	___/___	___/___	___/___
Visa 2	___/___	___/___	___/___	___/___
MasterCard 1	___/___	___/___	___/___	___/___
MasterCard 2	___/___	___/___	___/___	___/___
American Express	___/___	___/___	___/___	___/___
Discover Card	___/___	___/___	___/___	___/___
Gas Card 1	___/___	___/___	___/___	___/___
Gas Card 2	___/___	___/___	___/___	___/___
Dept. Store Card 1	___/___	___/___	___/___	___/___
Dept. Store Card 2	___/___	___/___	___/___	___/___
Finance Co. 1	___/___	___/___	___/___	___/___
Finance Co. 2	___/___	___/___	___/___	___/___
Credit Line	___/___	___/___	___/___	___/___
Student Loan 1	___/___	___/___	___/___	___/___
Student Loan 2	___/___	___/___	___/___	___/___
Other _______	___/___	___/___	___/___	___/___
Other _______	___/___	___/___	___/___	___/___

Irregular Income Planning (Instructions)

Many people have an "irregular" income, which simply means that their compensation fluctuates from month to month. This is especially common for the self-employed, as well as commission-based salespeople. While this makes it more difficult to predict your income, you are still responsible for doing a monthly budget!

The "Monthly Cash Flow Plan" (Form 5) should remain a crucial part of your plan, as it lays out exactly how much money you need to bring home each month to survive and prosper. However, instead of doing the "Allocated Spending Plan" (Form 7), you will use this "Irregular Income Planning" sheet.

On this form, simply look at the individual items from your "Monthly Cash Flow Plan" sheet and prioritize them by importance. Ask yourself, "If I only have enough money to pay one thing, what would that be?" Put that at the top of your list. Then, ask yourself, "If I only have enough money to pay one more thing, what would that be?" That's number two. Keep this up all the way down the list.

With your list in place, you're ready to get paid. If you get a $1,500 paycheck, you will spend that $1,500 right down the list until it is gone, recording the cumulative amount spent in the "Cumulative Amount" column. At that point, you're finished spending, no matter what remains unpaid on the list. That's why the most important things are at the top of the list, right?

Be prepared to stand your ground. Things usually have a way of seeming *important* when they are only *urgent*. For example, a once-in-a-lifetime opportunity to see your favorite band perform live may seem *important*, but in reality, it is only *urgent*, meaning that it is time-sensitive. Urgency alone should not move an item to the top of this list!

Irregular Income Planning (Form 8)

Item	Amount	Cumulative Amount

Extra copies of this form can be found online at **daveramsey.com/fpumember.**

Breakdown of Savings (Form 9)

After you have fully funded your emergency fund, you can start to save for other items, such as furniture, car replacement, home maintenance, or a vacation. This sheet will remind you that every dollar in your savings account is already committed to something. For example, it's a bad idea to take money away from car repairs to pay for an impulse Hawaiian vacation, even if you pay cash for it. What would you do if the car broke down the week you got back home? However, it can be okay to reassign the dollars to another category, as long as you do it on purpose and it doesn't put you in a pinch in another category. Keep up with your breakdown of savings every month, one quarter at a time.

Item		**Balance By Month**		
		________	________	________
Emergency Fund (1)	$1,000	________	________	________
Emergency Fund (2)	3-6 months	________	________	________
Retirement Fund		________	________	________
College Fund		________	________	________
Real Estate Taxes		________	________	________
Homeowner's Insurance		________	________	________
Repairs or Mn. Fee		________	________	________
Replace Furniture		________	________	________
Car Insurance		________	________	________
Car Replacement		________	________	________
Disability Insurance		________	________	________
Health Insurance		________	________	________
Doctor		________	________	________
Dentist		________	________	________
Optometrist		________	________	________
Life Insurance		________	________	________
School Tuition		________	________	________
School Supplies		________	________	________
Gifts (incl. Christmas)		________	________	________
Vacation		________	________	________
Other ____________________		________	________	________
Other ____________________		________	________	________
TOTAL		________	________	________

PERF HERE - DO NOT PRINT

Debt Snowball (Instructions)

Now it's time to knock out that debt! List your debts in order, from the smallest balance to the largest. Don't be concerned with interest rates, unless two debts have a similar payoff balance. In that case, list the one with the higher interest rate first. As you start eliminating debts, you'll start to build some serious momentum. These quick wins will keep you motivated, so you'll be able to stay on track.

The idea of the snowball is simple: pay minimum payments on all of your debts except for the smallest one. Then, attack that one with gazelle intensity! Every extra dollar you can get your hands on should be thrown at that smallest debt until it is gone. Then, you attack the second one. Every time you pay a debt off, you add its old minimum payment to your next debt payments. So, as the snowball rolls over, it picks up more snow. Get it?

Redo this sheet every time you pay off a debt so that you can see how close you're getting to total debt freedom. Keep the old sheets for encouragement—or to wallpaper the bathroom in your debt-free house someday!

The "New Payment" is the total of the previous debt's payment PLUS the current debt's minimum. As these payments compound, you'll start making huge payments as you work down the list. To factor in interest rates and calculate the exact date you will become DEBT FREE, use our online debt snowball tool at daveramsey.com/fpumember (available throughout your 13-week FPU class).

Debt Snowball (Form 10)

Item	Total Payoff	Minimum Payment	New Payment

PERF HERE - DO NOT PRINT

Pro Rata Debt List (Instructions)

"Pro rata" means the fair share, or the percent of your total debt each creditor represents. This will determine how much you should send them when you cannot make the minimum payments. Even if you cannot pay your creditors what they request, you should pay everyone as much as you can. Send the check for their pro rata share, along with a copy of your budget and this form, every month. *Do this even if the creditor says they will not accept it.*

Do you need to use the pro rata plan?

First, use your monthly cash flow plan to determine your total disposable income. Simply write down your income on the line at the top of the form. Then, write down the total you spend on necessities (not including consumer debt) each month. Subtract the necessity expense from the income, and you are left with your disposable income. This is the money you have to put toward your debts.

Second, add up your total amount of debt, not including your home, and write that in the blank provided. Below that, write in the total of the minimum monthly payments on all your debts. If the total of your minimum payments is greater than your total disposable income, you need to use the pro rata plan.

For example, Joe and Suzie have a total debt of $2,000, with a combined total minimum payment of $310. However, this family only has $200 in disposable income each month, which means they do not have enough money to make the minimum payments. So, they will use the pro rata plan to give each creditor their fair share of the family's $200.

How to Use This Form

This form has six columns:

1. **Item:** the name and type of the account.
2. **Total Payoff:** the total amount due on the account.
3. **Total Debt:** the combined total of all your debts.
4. **Percent:** the portion of the total debt load that each account represents. You can calculate this by simply dividing the Total Payoff by the Total Debt for each line.
5. **Disposable Income:** the amount of money you have left after paying necessities.
6. **New Payment:** the amount that you will now send to each creditor. You calculate this by multiplying the numbers in each line's Percent and Disposable Income columns.

The pro rata plan helps you to meet your obligations to the best of your ability. Of course, your creditors will not like receiving less than their required minimum payments. However, if you keep sending them checks, they'll most likely keep cashing them. We have had clients use this plan, even when sending only $2, who have survived for years.

Pro Rata Debt List (Form 11)

Income ______

Necessity Expense – ______

Disposable Income = ______

Total Debt: ______

Total Monthly Payments: ______

Item	Total Payoff		Total / Debt		= Percent		Disposable x Income		New = Payment
		/		=		X		=	
		/		=		X		=	
		/		=		X		=	
		/		=		X		=	
		/		=		X		=	
		/		=		X		=	
		/		=		X		=	
		/		=		X		=	
		/		=		X		=	
		/		=		X		=	
		/		=		X		=	
		/		=		X		=	
		/		=		X		=	
		/		=		X		=	
		/		=		X		=	
		/		=		X		=	
		/		=		X		=	
		/		=		X		=	
		/		=		X		=	

PERF HERE - DO NOT PRINT

Monthly Retirement Planning (Form 12)

Too many people use the READY-FIRE-AIM approach to retirement planning. That's a bad plan. You need to aim first. Your assignment is to determine how much per month you should be saving at 12% interest in order to retire at 65 with the amount you need.

If you save at 12% and inflation is at 4%, then you are moving ahead of inflation at a net of 8% per year. If you invest your nest egg at retirement at 12% and want to break even with 4% inflation, you will be living on 8% income.

Step 1: Annual income (today) you wish to retire on: ______________

Divide by .08

(Nest egg needed)equals: ______________

Step 2: To achieve that nest egg you will save at 12%, netting 8% after inflation. So, we will target that nest egg using 8%.

Nest Egg Needed $ ______________

Multiply by Factor X ______________

Monthly Savings Needed = ______________

Note: Be sure to try one or two examples if you wait 5 or 10 years to start.

8% Factors (select the one that matches your age)

Your Age	Years to Save	Factor
25	40	.000286
30	35	.000436
35	30	.000671
40	25	.001051
45	20	.001698
50	15	.002890
55	10	.005466
60	5	.013610

Monthly College Planning (Form 13)

In order to have enough for college, you must aim at something. Your assignment is to determine how much per month you should be saving at 12% interest in order to have enough for college.

If you save at 12% and inflation is at 4%, then you are moving ahead of inflation at a net of 8% per year.

Step 1: In today's dollars, the annual cost of the college of your choice is:

Amount per year $ ______________

X 4 years = $ ______________

(hint: $15,000 to $25,000 annually)

Step 2: To achieve that college nest egg, you will save at 12%, netting 8% after inflation. So, we will target that nest egg using 8%.

Nest Egg Needed $ ______________

Multiply by Factor X ______________

Monthly Savings Needed = ______________

Note: Be sure to try one or two examples if you wait 5 or 10 years to start.

8% Factors (select the one that matches your child's age)

Child's Age	Years to Save	Factor
0	18	.002083
2	16	.002583
4	14	.003287
6	12	.004158
8	10	.005466
10	8	.007470
12	6	.010867
14	4	.017746

Credit Card History (Form 14)

CARD NAME	NUMBER	ADDRESS	PHONE #	CLOSED	WRITTEN CONFIRMATION REQUESTED	WRITTEN CONFIRMATION RECEIVED
Visa	1234 567989 12	1234 Poplar Grove, suite 130	123-456-7890	09/21/06	09/21/06	11/21/06

Credit Card History (Form 14)

CARD NAME	NUMBER	ADDRESS	PHONE #	CLOSED	WRITTEN CONFIRMATION REQUESTED	WRITTEN CONFIRMATION RECEIVED

Extra copies of this form can be found online at **daveramsey.com/fpumember.**

Insurance Coverage Recap (Form 15)

TYPE	COMPANY	PLAN ID #	POLICY #	AMOUNT	AGENT	PHONE #
Term life	ABC Inurance	1234 567989 12	1234 567989 12	$450,000	John Smith	456-7890

Mortgage Information

TYPE	COMPANY	PLAN ID #	POLICY #	AMOUNT	AGENT	PHONE #

Extra copies of this form can be found online at **daveramsey.com/fpumember.**

Insurance Coverage Recap (Form 15)

TYPE	COMPANY	PLAN ID #	POLICY #	AMOUNT	AGENT	PHONE #

Mortgage Information

TYPE	COMPANY	PLAN ID #	POLICY #	AMOUNT	AGENT	PHONE #

Extra copies of this form can be found online at **daveramsey.com/fpumember.**

Dave Ramsey's Financial Peace University